MARGARET ROBERTS' BOOK OF HERBS

Margaret Roberts'
Book of Herbs

The medicinal and culinary uses of herbs in South Africa

Illustrated by Joan van Gogh

Southern Book Publishers

ISBN 1 86812 109 7

First published in 1983 by
Jonathan Ball Publishers
Second impression 1984
Third impression 1985
Fourth impression 1986
Fifth impression 1986

First edition, first impression 1988
First edition, second impression 1990

Published by
Southern Book Publishers (Pty) Ltd
PO Box 548
Bergvlei
2012

Design and phototypesetting by Book Productions, Pretoria
Printed and bound by National Book Printers, Goodwood, Cape

To those who care

Man, ever desirous of knowledge, has already explored many things; but more and greater still remain concealed; perhaps reserved for far distant generations, who shall prosecute the examination of their Creator's work in remote countries and make many discoveries for the pleasure and convenience of life.

Posterity shall see its increasing Museums, and the knowledge of the Divine Wisdom, flourish together; and at the same time all the practical sciences shall be enriched; for we cannot avoid thinking that what we know of the Divine works are much fewer than those of which we are ignorant.

Carl Linnaeus (1707–1778)

CONTENTS

FOREWORD

Margaret Roberts is one of those rare human beings who knows what life is all about and lives it to the full. A farmer's wife and mother of three teenage children, Margaret manages to cram a lot into her busy days. Not only is she a dedicated herb grower but also a successful potter, and I know that this book was written in the early hours of the morning – before her official day began.

When I first met Margaret I fell in love with her wonderful ability to communicate with people and her zest for life. Her delight in herbs and her knowledge of them has never ceased to amaze me.

This book had to be written. Without realizing it Margaret has been preparing for it for years. In addition to studying herbs in books, she has also grown them, worked with them, used them and healed with them. Her research has not only covered exotic herbs but more particularly our indigenous varieties and the recently opened physic garden at her farm Olifantshoek in the Magaliesberg, near Rustenburg, is unique in South Africa. Visitors from all over the country call in to see the garden every week.

Margaret's love of herbs is total and encompasses all of their many facets, from medicinal to culinary and from fragrances to fun and fairies. Fun is in fact very important in her life and if she is the witch she claims to be she is a very humorous one whose large brown eyes look out on life with a rather amused gaze.

A spiritual lady, who drew her love of gardening and art from her mother and an interest in philosophy from her father, Margaret loves people and it has been her ability to bring herbs and people together which has qualified her to write this excellent book about one of the oldest classes of plant life on earth. Margaret Roberts' *Book of Herbs* will prove popular with both hobbyist and specialist alike.

Keith E Kirsten

PREFACE

Long ago and far away, when life was quieter, more satisfying, more tranquil and more natural, there nestled at the foot of a great mountain a little whitewashed farmhouse. Days on the farm were filled with activity – crops were sown and harvested, the cows were milked and butter and soft cheeses made, flowers were cultivated and dried and made into country pot-pourris and pomanders. Long walks were taken and, with the passing of the seasons, many different plants were gathered and used until they became integrated into this simple, gentle life.

Then our children were born and, being far from towns and the harsh and pressing world, they learned those simple country pleasures that gave so much gentleness and satisfaction.

They planted gardens of vegetables and herbs and their own choice of flowers and they grew as their plants grew and they learned those little precious things that are never written down but which become a part of a quality of life that is fast fading.

All through the summer months we picked and stored the flowers. We made and enjoyed jams and jellies, salads, pies and tarts and bottled and dried fresh vegetables for winter use. Everything had a season.

In the firelit winter evenings sketchbooks were taken out and diaries written in; leaves and grasses were pressed and used in making cards and pictures. Everyone became totally involved in all those natural things.

All the beloved and almost forgotten recipes were carefully written down and the country things were a constant joy in our lives. School holidays were filled with that involvement in nature with which the children had grown up.

This peaceful, joyful lifestyle slowly started to disappear as the children grew up and went away to school. The hand-ground wheat and fragrant baked loaves gave way to bakery bread. The home-made soaps were replaced with supermarket brands, and the bottled fruits and vegetables started to give way to market bought produce. Life became filled with tension and rush and anxiety. There was no time any more to watch the seasons come and go. Too many people discovered the little farm pottery studio, demands became greater and greater, the tranquil lives were governed by timetables and exams and school sports and visitors and pressure, pressure, pressure.

Then suddenly one day it all became too much. We were letting go of all our natural things. We were allowing the harsh world to take over; we were letting anxiety rule us.

It had to stop. We had to go back to our natural way of life. If we didn't something within us would be gone forever. We had to withdraw and push away those pressures that were making us desperate and tired, ill and miserable.

Now the wheel has turned and, although the pressures of life are still there and the children are away from home for long periods, we still keep the farm fires burning with real wood and the house filled with the warm smell of home-baked bread and the gardens alive with vegetables and flowers. But best of all, we have also written it all down in a 'country notebook', so that these precious country ways will never be forgotten. This book is not only for our childrens' children; it is also a chance to share with those who care the real things that make life special and so well worth living.

There are thousands of magical cures growing in your very own garden, edging your pathways and hiding in your rockeries, simply waiting for you to take notice and learn to use them. Man is once again beginning to turn to nature as an alternative source of medication.

My intention is not to prescribe plant medicines for curing afflictions, nor am I trying to replace the doctor; rather I wish to reveal the amazing wealth in our green heritage and the wonderful uses that the plant kingdom has given us. Man has experimented with plant food and medicine for hundreds of years and today some of the most highly prized drugs are heritages from the dim past. We must not allow that past to be swallowed up in a plastic world. It is necessary to feel again the sand between our toes and the starlight on our faces, the summer breezes fresh and pure in our lungs, and our bodies nourished with real fresh food from the good earth.

In these pages I hope the reader will find pleasure and surprise, for one cannot but marvel at our plant kingdom and the wonderful healing properties that so many plants contain.

We, at the end of this twentieth century, find ourselves probing more and more into the natural things. Perhaps within the next decade or two medicine will have done an about-face and we will all be familiar with herbal medicine.

I have chosen to discuss the herbs and plants that are common to South Africans, those which grow readily in most areas of our country.

Most rewarding of all, and I hope the reader is deeply enough inspired to do so, is the making of a herb garden, for therein lies the real and true pleasure.

In the sixteenth century (and this was the time when the most beautiful herb gardens were cultivated) the belief was that the ground set aside for the garden should be rectangular or square, walled or fenced, with crossed paths at intervals, to scare away the devil. To record the sunny hours a sundial was a necessity and, at its foot, these words were carved in stone:

'Give light to them that walk in darkness
And guide our feet into the paths of peace.'

Then rosemary would be planted, either as a hedge surrounding the garden just inside the walk or a bush or two in each corner, to repel evil spirits.

A speckled toad would be coaxed and encouraged to reside in each of the four sections to protect the young herbs and the left horn of an ox would be burned at night 'to keep the dark mists and frosts without'.

An urn containing eagles' feathers was included to encourage the new growth of the plants after the winter and elder trees were planted conspicuously to keep the witches away. A box hedge was often planted along the paths and at the entrance to bring the witches up short should they be clever enough to enter. A witch would have to count the leaves in the hedge before moving on!

Whether or not these old customs are incorporated in your own herb garden the enchantment is still there and the laying out of it will bring much pleasure and excitement.

Nicholas Culpeper published his *Herbal* in 1652 and he summed up his concept of herbalism thus:

> 'What remains but that you labour to glorify God in your several places and do good yourselves first by increasing your knowledge, and to your neighbours afterwards by helping their infirmities; some such, I hope, this nation is worthy of and to all such I will be a friend during life, ready of my poor power to help.'

A whole new world is opening up to those touched by the magic wand of herbs – be it a plantain flowering stalk or a ten-notched yew tree branch!

Tranquillity is quickly and easily found by sitting quietly in the herb garden, resting the eyes on the soft, muted greens, greys and blues of the healing plants. To so many who have sat in my own herb garden the realization that perhaps the fairies or the gnomes or the plant souls are marching out to them fills them with wonder. They have assured me that if there are little people and spirits about, then in this herb garden they will be found!

When the day has been too full, too rushed, too anxiety filled, too frustrating to have achieved anything worthwhile, on those days my prayer is 'Please help me to remember, God, that nothing can happen to me today that You and I, together, can't handle'.

Then the stars come out and there is nothing more for you to do but sit quietly on the green lawn, look up at the stars, take ten deep long breaths – breathing out slowly, feel the starlight upon you, feel it soaking into you – so necessary for our soul's development, our consciousness and our inner growth.

Surely this must be one of the reasons why the wild things show so few illnesses and growth problems? Smell the summer night. The heat of the day will have released the aromatic oils of all the fragrant herbs and flowers. Breathe deeply and rhythmically; let all those cares of the day fall away. There is a huge comforting presence about you. After a while you will feel relaxed and will sleep easily and well.

William Coles, writing in the seventeenth century, said: 'If every Herb shows that there is a God, as verily it doth, the very beauty of plants being an argument that they are from an Intellectual Principle, what lectures of divinity might we receive from them if we would but attend diligently to the inward understanding of them?'

Throughout this book I have aimed at accuracy but to suppose that there are no mistakes would be arrogant. However, I trust that there will be so few as not to detract from its usefulness.

ACKNOWLEDGEMENTS

Long ago Keith Kirsten took a very small seed and sowed it in my mind with his usual enthusiasm. Writer Owen Reid watered that little seed with more enthusiasm and encouragement, urged me to put pen to paper and led me to Jonathan Ball.

Pamela Gunn took the untidy pages of my 5 a.m. scribblings and typed them out, and with more enthusiasm and persistence tied my leg to the table so that I *had* to write.

San Marie Harms spent many hours drawing plants and teaching me to see their beauty through her observant eyes. She opened a new world for me, a world in which I blossomed.

Joan van Gogh, in the shortest time, painted botanical replicas to enable the reader to identify each plant easily and surely.

Alison Lowry edited and pruned and calmly put everything in order, leaving a green and growing matured plant alive and well and standing alone. To her my most appreciative sounds are uttered.

So I thank them, all seven, for their parts in the plan and the sprinkling of persistence, determination and enthusiasm they watered into the green magic.

For my family and friends who encouraged and enthused, who helped and who held out hands of love and friendship and the warmness of sunlight, my warmest thanks to you all.

ALL YEAR ROUND

ROCK ROSE

Cistus villosus

This is an aromatic plant that has varying coloured flowers. The small, single, frail flowers have a somewhat creased appearance. The age old reputation of a brew of the flowers curing timidity in children is still effective today.

The ancient remedy was to steep rock rose flowers in a shallow glass dish of well water. The dish was placed in the sunlight and moonlight for three days and nights and then, early in the morning and in the evening before going to bed, a dessert-spoonful of the brew was taken.

The rock rose is considered to be beneficial in the treatment of cancer and it is used as a calming and soothing remedy in homoeopathic medicine.

As a gargle for sore, ulcerated throats it is comforting. A brew is made of the leaves and flowers, one handful to half a litre of boiling water, and allowed to steep before straining. To calm and relax, a tablespoon of the brew should be taken three times daily. The same brew is effective as a wash for venereal diseases.

Rock rose is a safe remedy and can be given to children to still their fears and to give them courage and confidence. A dessertspoon morning and night of the above-mentioned brew is recommended. My favourite way is still to use the sun- and moon-soaked flowers as they did so long ago.

In the heat of the day the leaves of the rock rose give off a sticky, sweet-scented gum called labdanum. Long ago, shaggy goats were put out to graze on the rock rose covered hillsides in Crete and Cyprus and the labdanum was combed from their beards in the evenings. Special rakes of leather thongs were dragged over the leaves and the sticky mass adhering to the thongs was scraped off and formed into cakes and then sun-dried.

Labdanum is also a perfume fixative and is much valued as an ingredient in ec-clesiastical incense.

WILDE ALS

Artemisia affra

Wild Wormwood, Lengana (TSWANA), Mhlonyane (ZULU), Umhlonyane (XHOSA), Zengana (SOUTHERN SOTHO)

Wilde als is one of the most widely used plants in the popular medicines in South Africa, by both black and white alike.

The old remedies for coughs and colds, chills, stomach-ache, dry dyspepsia, croup, whooping cough, gout and for use as a purgative are still as effective today.

The leaves are made into a tea and can be sweetened with honey or sugar, and this tea is especially good for bronchial ailments and coughs.

A bath made by steeping handfuls of leaves in boiling water and then straining the hot brew will bring out the rash in measles and may also be used to bathe haemorrhoids.

A strong warm brew can be dropped gently into the ear to relieve earache; it can be held in the mouth for toothache and gumboils or can be taken internally for fevers and blood poisoning.

The vapour from boiling the leaves in a kettle can be inhaled for bronchitis and respiratory infections; Africans use the same vapour for menstrual chill and after childbirth.

The Tswanas on our farm roll a fresh leaf and insert it into the nostril to relieve colds and headaches. They also pack a hollow tooth with a leaf for toothache relief.

For mumps swellings and for neuralgia a leaf compress, warmed and bound in place, is comforting. It is helpful for soothing colic in children, where an infusion is sipped and the warmed leaves are bound over the abdomen.

The dried leaves smoked are helpful for sore throats and congested lungs, and for throat irritation and night coughing.

In the south-western Cape an infusion made of the leaves and tips of the stems is used as an eye lotion as well as for coughs and colds and as a wash for measles.

The Zulu use the ground-up plant in water as an enema for children and, internally, as a blood and skin cleanser.

A common brew made by many whites consists of mixing brandy, sugar, thyme, ginger, rosemary and mint with the wilde als. This brew is used for coughs and bronchitis and stomach ailments. The brandy preserves the herbs, giving the brew a long shelf life.

Wilde als grows easily and seeds itself readily. It remains green all the year round. Our herdboys collect armfuls along the mountain slopes and bring them to the farmhouse in the summer months for the moth repellent sachets that are made during the winter. The strong, pungent smell of the plant repels moths and other insects and is surprisingly pleasant when added to pot-pourris.

Africans very often add the dried leaves to other wild herbs for a health-giving tea and through the winter drink pure wilde als tea as an influenza preventative.

3

Leaves may be packed into the shoes to help against sweating and sore feet and, after a long journey, leaves rubbed over the feet give quick relief to travel-weary bones.

BULRUSH

Typha latifolia forma capensis

Palmiet, Matjiesgoed, Ibhuma (ZULU), Umkhanzi (XHOSA), Motsitla (SOTHO)

The flowering period of the bulrush is from December to February and it grows with ease and abundance in dams and vleis, along furrows and in marshy places. It is used for thatching and weaving and mat-making by all African peoples. In the dry summers their children can be seen under the trees, near a dam, weaving their own mats as bulrushes are easily pulled out of the receding water.

The Zulus use a decoction of the root in the treatment of venereal diseases and the Xhosa use a similar decoction to aid the placenta removal in childbirth. The Southern Sotho use the whole plant in the making of a medicine which is taken during labour; it is believed to strengthen uterine contractions.

The woolly inflorescence is used in the treatment of wounds and burns by the people living in the Philippines and some of the old Tswana say that their people also used the woolly, dry seed fluff to staunch bleeding by packing the wound with it.

The rootstock is used as a diuretic and has for many years been used in the treatment of dysentery and bowel haemorrhages, as well as urethritis.

In the Antilles the seed fluff is used for the treatment of burns.

The pith of the stalk can be eaten and was once regarded as a famine food. It has a rather unattractive taste and texture so it could only have been consumed in dire circumstances!

The female seed head becomes a deep velvety brown and, if picked as soon as it ripens and kept in a vase of water for several weeks, the head does not disintegrate and can be used for many years as an indoor arrangement.

KWEEKGRAS

Cynodon dactylon

Quickgras, Buffelgras, Handekweek, Wiregrass, Running Grass, Indian Couch, Couch Grass, Mothowa (TSWANA), Umqambalala (ZULU), Morara (SOTHO)

This invasive, tough, grow-anywhere grass is so soundly cursed that it is difficult to believe it has medicinal properties. It can be made into the hard-wearing lawn of most farms but it is so invasive that it should be well considered before planting.

Medicinally, whites in the Transvaal use the leaf blades and young tips for heartburn. These are bruised and mixed with bicarbonate of soda. The bruised plant is used as a styptic to wounds and the Xhosa use the bruised and macerated stems and leaf blades as a dressing on swellings and sores. A lotion made by boiling the stems and leaf blades is used as a wash for wounds and a decoction of the root was once used by the 1820 settlers as a blood purifier as well as a remedy for indigestion.

The grass is used by the Sotho as a charm against sorcery and can be mixed with other herbs as a protective charm.

A decoction of the entire plant is used in the Philippines as a diuretic and in India it is still medicinally used today as a digestive treatment.

The leaf blade contains vitamin C and minerals as well as cynodin and triticin, a carbohydrate. Its value is therefore far greater than one might expect from its appearance.

Kweekgras is very easily propagated. Any small piece of runner grows quickly and a good thick lawn can result in about six weeks in the summer.

IVY

Hedera helix

Ivy, a pleasing evergreen climber and ground cover, does well under trees or on shady walls, and looks attractive throughout the year.

With other members of the *Araliaceae* family, ivy originally grew at the southern tip of South America and in Australia; its flowering period therefore – small and insignificant honey-coloured flowers – is in the summer in the southern hemisphere.

The ivy has many medicinal uses, from the treatment of headaches, eye and ear infections, down to curing corns on the toes. It is even supposed to prevent intoxication! Dionysus wore a wreath of vine and ivy leaves and the ivy still climbs up the outside of many old English pubs.

The leaf infused in water is an excellent eye-wash for man and animal but, as it is a potent herb, it should always be used in small quantities. A standard brew is 10 leaves to 1 litre of water, this same brew being used as an eye-wash and taken internally. Two tablespoons before meals will help heal glandular complaints, mumps, inflamed and swollen joints and jaundice, as well as reduce fevers. However, as ivy is poisonous, great care should be taken not to exceed the specified quantity.

A brew made from the pulped leaves and berries, added to olive oil and left in the sun for a few hours, is used as a rub for sciatica and swollen joints.

Another brew made from ivy leaves, crushed and added to warmed vinegar and rosewater in equal quantities, can be very soothing and may relieve headaches and tension. Apply a cloth which has been soaked in the brew to the forehead.

The sticky juice or resin from the stem may be used to get rid of unwanted hair. Some African tribes use it as an aphrodisiac.

A glucoside, saponin, is present in the leaf and a handful of leaves added to the water when washing clothes will help remove stains from fabrics. Woollen suits and skirts that have developed a shine can have the shine reduced by using a cloth wrung out in ivy water when pressing.

Juice extracted from the leaves was used as black hair dye in olden days. Gypsies used crushed, boiled ivy leaves for burns, packing them on top of the burn and keeping them moist with the water in which the leaves were boiled.

Crushed leaves soaked in vinegar, to which a little salt has been added, wrapped and bound over a corn, will soften and ease it so that it can be quickly removed. The same treatment is used for cancerous growths, applied two or three times daily or left on overnight. Chopped fresh leaves, moistened with a little water, can be applied as a poultice for sciatica.

Ivy cuttings root quickly and, as ivy withstands winter's cold, it makes a useful ground cover as well as a pot-plant.

ST JOHN'S WORT

Hypericum perforatum

Touch and Heal

This is a garden plant in South Africa but in England it is found growing along the waysides and in woodlands.

The bright yellow, poppy-form flowers, steeped in sun-warmed olive oil, yield the famous 'oil of St John's wort' used as far back as the time of the Crusades.

The entire plant has healing properties. Grown near the home it is believed to protect the home from harm and loss and in former times was much used in magic charms. Bringing bunches of its flowers into the house was believed would encourage fairies to visit.

The leaves have light specks on them and when held up to the light these specks can be plainly seen. They are the oil glands (or the holes the devil pricked to let out the goodness). The extracted oil is known in the United States as 'red oil' and is extensively used in the local application to cuts and bruises.

In Europe it is still used in the treatment of dysentery, phthisis, sciatica, rabies and again is also applied to wounds.

The entire plant – blossom, leaf, stalk – is antibiotic, and the antibiotic has been patented as a possible food preservative.

8

PAWPAW
Carica papaya

Mpapai (SWAHILI)

The pawpaw is a valuable source of food in all the tropical countries in which it flourishes, both for animals and humans alike. The ripe flesh is beneficial in the treatment of dysentery, and rubbing the inside of the skin onto warts often results in their disappearance. In Java eating the fruit is believed to ward off rheumatism.

The root, pounded and beaten and taken in hot water, is used to relieve kidney and bladder troubles; it is also used as an external remedy for haemorrhoids, and is held in position by bandages at night.

The leaf has many uses, its major one being the tenderising of meat. Steaks and chops wrapped in the leaves and left overnight in the refrigerator will be beautifully tender; alternatively the crushed dried seeds or pips can be sprinkled lightly over tough meat and allowed to marinate for a few hours in an oil and vinegar sauce. When cooked, the meat will be full of flavour, tender and juicy.

The young leaf can also be eaten as a vegetable and should be lightly steamed. It also contains saponin and can be used as a soap substitute to remove stains from the skin and from clothing. The milky juice can be warmed and applied to boils to draw them, with a warmed leaf bound over the boil.

In Hawaii the fruit is used for skin infections and the leaf and juice for dressing wounds. The leaf is also sometimes used as a laxative.

Both the male and female flowers have their uses. They are delicious dipped into a sugar and water syrup and dried, and eaten as a confection to treat respiratory ailments and summer coughs.

The leaf can be smoked too. It should be dried in the shade, shredded and rolled. It is used in the treatment of asthma.

The unripe fruit is delicious as a vegetable when cooked with pumpkin and the young shoots and tendrils of the pumpkin vine.

The pith of the stem can be eaten raw and in the East Indies is used in times of famine.

The ripe fruit, full of vitamins and minerals, should be included in the diet whenever possible. Male and female trees should be planted close to one another. In Natal's coastal regions no garden should be without a few pawpaw trees as they grow so easily there.

In the more wooded areas some Natal gardeners use huge rubber snakes wound around the ripening fruit to frighten off marauding monkeys and nets and wire guards are all evidence that the pawpaw is a favourite fruit.

The juice contains an enzyme called papain which is currently being extensively researched. It is used in the United States for many things, including 'chill proofing' beer, tenderising meat and in the preparation of pre-cooked foods. It is also used in the manufacture of chewing gum, in the leather industry and in the shrinking of textiles, as well as in the medical field where it has been prescribed to assist protein digestion in chronic dyspepsia, gastritis and gastric fermentation.

ALFALFA

Medicago sativa

Lucerne

Alfalfa, usually known as lucerne, is a perennial rich in vitamins and minerals and is one of the most popular fodder crops. It is equally good for humans! It is an excellent tonic as it alkalises the entire system and cleanses the kidneys. Well known for the speed it gives to racehorses it is as effective for athletes.

The plant contains an enormous quantity of vitamin C, of which 80% is lost in drying it. It is also rich in vitamins A, K and E and should therefore be included in the diet from time to time.

When finely cut up and added to a salad, the young shoots and leaves taste a bit like green peas and make an appetising addition. A refreshing summer drink can be made from a handful of fresh lucerne to which boiling water is added, with a twist of orange peel and two sprigs of garden mint. This should be allowed to cool and then strained and sweetened with honey. Add some chipped ice and you will enjoy a reviving tonic in the heat of a summer afternoon.

Sprouted lucerne seeds make a delicious protein snack; mixed with mayonnaise and spread on homemade brown bread, they will fast become a family favourite.

King Darius, who ruled Persia from 521-486 BC, discovered lucerne and it was at his instigation that it was cultivated for fodder. The Chinese drink a brew made from lucerne as a cure for stomach ulcers.

TO SPROUT LUCERNE

Take ½ cup of seeds and cover with warm water. Leave overnight. In the morning drain (retain the liquid for soups or stews) and place the seeds in a jar. Cover with a cheesecloth square and tie. Turn the jar onto its side. Rinse the seeds twice daily by pouring lukewarm water into the jar, swirling around and pouring off excess. After 3-5 days place the jar on a windowsill to encourage the green leaf growth and thereafter keep in the refrigerator.

Use on salads, in omelettes, sprinkle over roasts and mix with cream cheese. Start the next batch on the third day, always rinsing the seeds thoroughly twice a day.

SOUR FIG

Carpobrotus edulis

Hottentot's Fig, Ikhambilamabulawo (ZULU)

The fruit and juice from the leaves of the sour fig have been widely used for generations. Juice from the pounded leaves contains antiseptic properties and may be used as a gargle for throat infections, mouth infections and sore throats of all kinds, as well as for indigestion and in the treatment of diarrhoea and dysentery.

The juice is strained through a fine sieve and is easily obtained by pounding the fleshy leaves in a pestle and mortar.

An old tuberculosis remedy was to use the juice from the leaves, together with olive oil and honey in equal parts, given in a wineglass three times a day.

Cloths soaked in the leaf juice are an excellent poultice for burns; the old 'Haarlem' remedy of lard, juice and castor oil melted together was also used as a dressing for burns.

In the Transvaal the Africans use a decoction of the leaf for a throat gargle in cases of diptheria, while an old Boer recipe called for equal parts vinegar, honey and leaf juice used as a gargle for sore throats.

The Hottentot women make an infusion of the fruit and drink it to ensure an easy birth. When the infant is born they smear the child with leaf juice to make it quick, nimble and strong.

The sour fig grows easily close to sand dunes at the coast and it is a convenient antidote to those nasty bluebottle stings which bathers so often experience. The leaf should be squeezed and rubbed over the afflicted area continuously for several minutes until the sting fades.

A jam can be made of the ripened fruit and the fruit can be eaten raw or dried for later use.

SOUR FIG CONSERVE

1 kg ripened sour figs
1 kg brown sugar
500 g raisins
2 oranges, peeled
juice of 2 lemons

Chop the orange peel, discarding the pulp. Cover peel, raisins and sour figs with 1 litre water for two hours. Boil in the water in which they were soaked. Add sugar and lemon juice and simmer until transparent and thick. This takes approximately one hour. A cup of chopped pecan nuts or walnuts can be added 5 minutes before the conserve is ready.

Bottle in hot, sterilized bottles, seal with wax paper soaked in brandy and screw the lids on firmly.

COMMON GROUNDSEL

Senecio vulgaris

Kruiskruie, Mohodu-ya-pela-o-monyenyane (SOUTHERN SOTHO)

Groundsel, an introduced species from Europe, has become a common garden weed in South Africa. The name comes from the old English 'ground swallower', while the French call it 'tout venue'. It was once widely used in Europe as an astringent and emmenagogue and is still today used to some extent in homoeopathy and as a wash for cuts and grazes.

Perhaps its best known use is as an appetizing addition to caged birds' diet which brings to mind the little poem that we as children so often recited:

> If dickybirds should buy and sell
> In common markets, I can tell
> The way they'd spend their money.
> They'd buy the pinkest worms for meat
> And common groundsel for a treat.
> Though you may think it funny
> Love me not or love me well,
> That's the way they'd buy and sell.

In England bunches of the weed were actually marketed as rabbit and cage bird food.

An infusion of the leaves and stems is used as an external application for chronic mastitis in cows and also for haemorrhoidal nodules. A green dye or colouring matter can also be made of the plant. The expressed juice was once used in the treatment of epilepsy and as a remedy for dysmenorrhoea. Large doses are dangerous to the liver, however, so this plant should only be used under medical supervision.

SAGE

Salvia officinalis

Salie, Bloublomsalie

Sage has been cultivated for hundreds of years and there are over 700 species widely distributed throughout the world. It gets its name from the Latin *salvere*, meaning to be in good health or to be well.

A sage tea is one of the most beneficial to mankind and the Chinese once exchanged their local teas with the Dutch for sage tea, believing that it endowed them with health and wisdom.

Sage tea is a proven cure for fevers, colds and sore throats. Even chewing a sage leaf will greatly relieve a sore throat. A sage tea brew is used in the treatment of digestive ailments, flatulence, lack of appetite, constipation and obesity, as well as for mental derangement, depression, anxiety and to improve the memory.

The pulped, chopped herb is beneficial if applied externally to ulcers, wounds and sores and will stop excessive bleeding. A strong brew rubbed into the scalp stimulates hair growth and it tones up the hair generally and also removes dandruff.

Sage leaves can act as a moth and insect deterrent if used in sachets or in pot-pourris in cupboards; even a bunch, tied together and hung in a cupboard, will do the trick.

Sage inhalations are excellent for congested noses and sinus conditions and sage leaves rubbed onto the teeth clean and whiten them, at the same time refreshing the mouth.

Chopped sage has long been used in poultry stuffings, in soups and in stews and the ancients consumed large quantities of sage in their ale and in their stews, believing that it ensured long life and clear thinking.

The red sage, *Salvia colorata*, is considered a 'cure-all' and is powerfully medicinal. It is used for relief of all respiratory conditions, including tuberculosis, and as a gargle for ulcers and sores in the mouth.

The oil extracted from sage is employed in both the culinary and pharmaceutical industries.

It is a potent herb and a teaspoon of chopped leaves to a cup of water is sufficient as a general treatment.

Feverish patients can be washed in a sage brew to help bring down the fever and a pleasantly flavoured tonic can be made by infusing sage leaves in water and leaving the brew in the sunlight for a day. It may then be used as a general pick-me-up tonic for depression and anxiety, as well as indigestion. I use the sage water for adding to cool drinks and for making tea and find it very calming and relaxing.

SAGE STUFFING FOR POULTRY

a handful of sage leaves
2 slices brown bread, crumbed
salt and pepper
juice of 2 lemons
30 ml debittered Torula yeast powder
125-200 ml plain yoghurt or sour cream

Combine all ingredients. Stuff the fowl and roast in the usual way.

I bake the bird in an unglazed gypsy pot with a lid that has been soaked in water for half an hour. Add a cup of water and a squeeze of lemon juice and a little salt and pepper and place in a cold oven. Bake for three hours at 180°C and the succulent flavour-filled result will spoil you forever – you will find this is the only way to cook poultry!

ROSEMARY

Rosmarinus officinalis

One of the best loved herbs, rosemary takes its name from the sea – dew of the sea – *Rosmarinus*. It is widely cultivated in gardens and is one of the most important of the aromatics.

It is also an excellent insecticide. Using 5 ml rosemary oil to 300 ml beer, this should be sprayed onto the problem area or plant. One can also powder the dried herb with equal quantities of dried wormwood and sprinkle it lightly in cupboards, along skirting boards or between and on rows of vegetables.

Rosemary is used to treat high blood pressure, as a general heart tonic – one of the few in fact that is not a drastic drug – as well as all ailments of the heart. It is an effective cure for headaches when taken as a strong tea, sweetened with honey.

Rosemary can be used as a hair lotion and rinse. It checks falling hair and generally stimulates and revitalises the hair and is effective in treating eczema of the scalp. Boil 6 large sprigs of rosemary in 1,25 litres of water. Strain and massage into the scalp. Use also as a final rinse after shampooing.

It is said that a sprig placed under the pillow of a sleeping child will prevent nightmares and it was believed essential to either surround the herb garden with rosemary or to plant a bush in all four corners to repel evil spirits!

A few sprigs of rosemary kept in your car, it is still believed, will protect the vehicle and its occupants, in the same way that gypsies used to hang sprigs in their wagons long ago.

The Romans believed it to be a sacred herb which brought happiness to the living and ensured peace to the dead.

It also used to be burned as an incense as it is antiseptic and in olden days it was regarded as 'good for seasoning meat and making sauces' – in fact as widely used in those days as it is now.

The most famous culinary formula, 'the Queen of Hungary water', brought rosemary into the limelight at the end of the fourteenth century. There are a great many variations on the formula and one may become confused but this essentially is the original.

'In the city of Buda, in the kingdom of Hungary, was found the present recipe in the Hours of Her Most Serene Highness, Princess Donna Izabella Queen of Hungary: I, Donna Izabella, aged 72, in firm of limb and afflicted with gout have for one whole year used the present recipe which was given to me by a Hermit I had never seen before nor seen since, which has had so great an effect on me that I recovered my health and regained my strength and on beholding my beauty, the King of Poland desired to marry me which I refused for the love of Our Lord Jesus

16

Christ, believing that the Receipt had been given me by an Angel:
Take 30 ozs. of Spirits of Wine, distilled four times [rectified alcohol], 20 ozs. of Rosemary Flowers. Put altogether in a tight, corked vessel for the space of 50 hours, then distil in a bain-marie. Take one dram [about 4 g] in the morning once a week with some other liqueur or drink, or else with meat [food]. And wash the face in it every morning and rub the infirm limbs with it.'

A more realistic elixir within the scope of us all is 600 g rosemary flowers plus the flowering tips of rosemary. Macerate 900 ml rectified alcohol in a glass jar; then expose the jar, making sure it is well stoppered, to the sun for at least one month, shaking it frequently. Finally strain the mixture and press through a fine cloth. Use it as Donna Izabella did!

Rosemary tea last thing before going to bed at night is excellent for relief of physical and mental strain and is also beneficial following a severe illness.

Nowadays it is being used more and more in the treatment of migraine, jaundice, fainting fits, vertigo, cirrhosis of the liver, gallstones, rheumatism and obesity. Make an infusion of the flowering tips, fresh or dried, 30–50 g to 1 litre of boiling water. Cover and leave to infuse for 10 minutes. Take one coffee cupful, warmed and sweetened with honey, after meals, except in the condition that affects the liver. In this case take one teacupful before breakfast, one teacupful before dinner and a coffee cupful before the midday meal.

ROSEMARY WINE
(Fortifying, digestive and antispasmodic)

200 g fresh rosemary leaves or 60 g dried leaves to 1 litre good red wine. Leave to infuse for 15 days, shaking from time to time. Strain and sweeten if desired. Take 1 sherry glassful after meals. It is especially good slightly warmed, taken after dinner or just before bedtime – most calming and restful.

TO REMOVE FRECKLES AND WRINKLES

50 g flowering rosemary tips
½ litre white wine.

Boil for two minutes. Leave to infuse for 1 hour. Strain and apply as a lotion morning and night on a pad of cottonwool.

ROSEMARY NERVE TONIC

1 bottle good red wine
Steep in this:

1 sprig rosemary
6 candied cherries
1 dozen raisins
1 piece ginger root
1 sprig wormwood
2 nutmegs
1 piece cinnamon bark

Steep for one week keeping it in a warm place and shaking the bottle daily. Strain and take a small wineglassful after dinner each night.

ROSEMARY WONDER WATER
(Especially good for old people and as a tonic after illness. Good as a pick-me-up too.)

2 sprigs dried rosemary
1 bottle claret
5 ml nutmeg
1 piece ginger root
1 cinnamon stick

Crush ingredients finely in a mortar, and steep in claret. Leave for a fortnight. Strain through muslin, re-cork and keep for a month. Then drink a wineglassful each day.

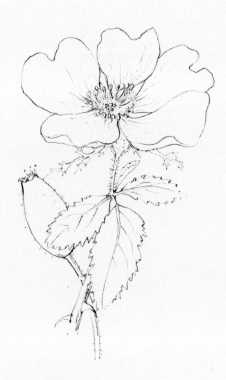

1 Rose-scented geranium *(Pelargonium graveolens)*
2 Lemon verbena *(Aloysia triphylla)*
3 Lavender *(Dentata)*
4 Lavender *(Lavendula spica)*

1

2

3

4

WILD OLIVE

Olea africana

Olienhout, Motlhware (TSWANA), Umquma (ZULU), Motholoari (SOTHO)

Perhaps the wild olive could be said to be a herb tree as it is so extensively used medicinally by all tribes, and it seems that every part of the tree is valuable to man.

The leaf is used as an eye lotion for man and animal both by whites and many African tribes.

The Thlaping drink a decoction made from the fresh bark of the wild olive to relieve colic. The Xhosa use a strong leaf brew as a gargle for diptheria and sore throats. A decoction made from the grated root and scraped bark is used for urinary and bladder infections by the Xhosa, the Zulu and the Sotho and is also used as a cure for headaches.

The juice of the ripe black olive is an effective ink substitute. The Tswana use the same juice as a corn softener. This is effected by frequently squeezing the juice onto the afflicted area.

Cattle, goats and sheep all browse the leaves, particularly through the winter when the grass is dry (the wild olive is an evergreen).

The Masai drink a tea made from the heart-wood for cleansing the blood and they believe it to be strength giving. The twigs and dried leaves make an excellent fumigant when burned. This method is used by the Tswana in the Thabazimbe area.

The fruit, although bitter and astringent, is enjoyed by man, baboons and birds.

The pounded root, made into a tea, has also been used as a cure for rheumatism. The pieces should be well boiled first, then strained before drinking. It is not considered very effective nowadays however.

The timber from the wild olive is hard and durable. It is used for fencing posts and, because it is so hard, it is much favoured for spear handles, knobkerries and walking sticks. The stick is cut fresh from the tree and the outer bark peeled off, carved and left to cure and dry. As the wood is resistant to termites, fencing posts in most mountain camps are made of wild olive for they withstand weather and time extremely well. Wild olive wood also makes attractive furniture.

When the wood is burned it serves as a long lasting, pleasant scented fuel.

1 Job's tears *(Coix lacryma-jobi)*
2 Feverfew *(Chrysanthemum parthenium)*
3 Parsley *(Petroselinum crispum)*
4 Pyrethrum *(Chrysanthemum cinerarifolium)*

AJUGA
Ajuga ophrydis

Carpet Bugle

A perennial with a flowering period from October to January, this popular ground cover grows happily in many positions. I have it lushly growing under some thorn trees in the shade and its pretty blue flowers seem to bloom continuously. In the sun it is inclined to dry off in patches but it thrives when generously watered. I use the flowers for a touch of blue in pot-pourris.

It has long been considered a smallpox antidote by some African tribes. They take the ash from a burned plant and mix it with mutton fat. This is made into a ball and put onto sticks which are then stuck into the ground around the village.

A decoction of the root is used for bathing skin rashes.

There are several varieties of ajuga, a purple one, a silver and green variegated one and also a bronzy, multicoloured one. The roots of all varieties are equally effective for rashes and skin inflammations.

FIELD MALLOW

Malva parviflora

Wild Mallow, Kasie, Unomolwana (XHOSA), Qena, Tikamotse (SOTHO)

A decoction of the field mallow is still drunk today by whites and blacks alike as a nerve tonic.

In the Western Cape it was used long ago as a uterine douche and as a lotion for styes and for red, sore eyes.

The leaf is used today by the Xhosa and Sotho as a hot poultice for wounds, swellings and abscesses. The Xhosa also use a decoction as a wash for suppurating wounds and then bind on the hot leaves as a poultice to draw off the pus. The Southern Sotho use a decoction of the leaves as a tapeworm remedy, as well as for profuse menstruation. They also make a lotion which is soothing for bruised, swollen limbs. They give a decoction of the root to a person who has lost a near relative, believing he must not mix with others before drinking the medicine or terrible sores will break out on his body. They also use the leaves and stems, macerated and pounded, to repair broken earthenware pots.

The field mallow is considered poisonous to cattle and horses. After ingesting it they show symptoms of shivering or trembling before collapsing. Hens eating the plant produce pink whites in their eggs.

Field mallow grows sturdily everywhere and we should take heed of it as it is so useful and soothing for the treatment of swellings and abscesses. Leaves warmed in hot water and applied over a deeply embedded splinter will in no time ease it to the surface.

THYME

Thymus serpyllum, Thymus vulgaris

One of nature's antiseptics, both *Thymus serpyllum* and *Thymus vulgaris* are known for their ancient healing properties. Thyme walks are often found in old herb gardens. It was believed that when walked upon the spreading plants released their antiseptic properties into the air and these were said to combat plague and other infections.

The thyme species, and there are many, are native to Europe and grow wild in the Mediterranean countries. When burned they were used as an incense and fumigant in temples and other public places.

The Egyptians and Etruscans used thyme in their preparations for embalming the dead. In ancient Greece thyme was used to anoint the body and to add to water for bathing. It was considered a symbol of elegance and courage. The association of courage was especially strong at the time of the Crusades when the ladies would embroider a bee with a sprig of thyme on their knights' scarves as a symbol of bravery.

In the Western Cape a tincture of *Thymus serpyllum* is still used today as a remedy for diarrhoea and abdominal cramps, as well as for heart conditions. It is also used for whooping cough and respiratory conditions such as asthma in America and in South Africa.

The French use *Thymus serpyllum* as a decoction for skin conditions and itching and in Russia it is used for relief of neuralgia and rheumatism.

There are so many varieties of thyme that one is easily confused, but the only one suitable for beverages is lemon thyme. A very refreshing winter tea can be made with a few sprigs of lemon thyme. Allow it to steep a few minutes and then serve with a slice of lemon and sweeten with brown sugar, if desired.

I make an apricot tart to go with it with lemon thyme leaves in the pastry – an instant success with everyone.

LEMON THYME APRICOT TART

125 g melted butter
125 ml brown sugar
1 beaten egg
500 ml flour
10 ml lemon thyme leaves
10 ml baking powder
3 ml vanilla
pinch salt
250 ml apricot jam

Whisk egg, vanilla and sugar. Add sifted flour and baking powder alternately with melted butter. Add lemon thyme leaves. Knead well on floured board. Press ⁷/₈ of the mixture into a pie plate. Spread with apricot jam. Grate the remaining ¹/₈ of dough onto the jam. Bake at 180°C for 20–30 minutes. Serve with cream.

Thymus vulgaris is the common thyme of culinary use and is a frequent addition in South African cuisine. This plant has also been used extensively as an antiseptic, antispasmodic, carminative, digestive, emmenogogue and sedative, as well as a lotion, inhalation and enema! In short, it is a kind of panacea.

The fresh plant yields an oil known as thymol and this is used in medicine today as it is carminative and germicidal. It is used especially in the treatment of whooping cough, bronchitis, nervous derangements, hysteria, headaches, to control excessive menstruation and diseases of the uterus. It is also a safe remedy for worms, even in small children. A hot fomentation is an excellent healer of boils and abscesses and brings on perspiration in fevers.

In fact thyme seems to contain such amazing healing properties that one should never be without it.

Sprigs of thyme in a salad are beneficial; sprinkled over roasts and mixed into salad dressings it gives a delicious flavour. Thyme is almost as essential as salt in the diet.

The Bedouin Arabs make their well-known condiment Za'atar from dried thyme, crushed coriander, sesame seeds and rock salt. Pounded and mixed with olive oil, it is delicious on bread or used as a salad dressing.

The leaves of thyme, dried and powdered and taken like snuff, will clear a blocked or bleeding nose. An effective brew for coughs and bronchitis, influenza, chills or insomnia, is 1 handful of fresh thyme to 1 litre water, boiled until it has reduced to half the volume, and then sweetened with honey. One dessertspoonful every half hour should be sufficient.

A handful of thyme boiled in a litre of water, cooled, strained and rubbed into the scalp every day will prevent or arrest hair loss.

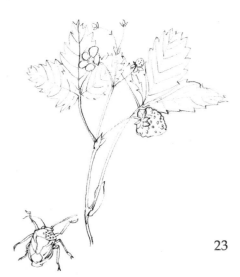

23

AGAVE

Agave americana

Century Plant

The giant agave provides one of the cheapest cattle fences available. It is a succulent monocotyledon and it flowers after several years, usually about ten, and then dies. We use the dried tree-like flowering stalk as a Christmas tree, sometimes painted white, and decorated with baubles. Standing in a large pot, it is perhaps more African than the traditional fir tree that South Africans still use at Christmas time. After Christmas I place the bare tree outside on the cool stoep and later hang it with pottery birds so that it continues to give pleasure throughout the year. One year we hung white clay doves on it and it became so popular we went into full dove production for several years to follow!

As the agave thrives upon arid soils, once it is planted it does not need much care and seems to propagate by seeds and suckers. The Karoo farmers make a dry extract from the leaf as a purge for farm animals and for the ostrich in particular. A leaf split and warmed can be applied locally for relief of pain in rheumatism and an infusion of the chopped leaf is a strong purgative.

The agave leaf is also used as an insecticide and wallpaper impregnated with the juice is termite and fishmoth resistant.

It can be used as stock food in times of drought and the pulped leaf, mixed with hay or mealie-meal, can be fed to most domestic stock. Some tests, however, have proved it to be poisonous to sheep.

The juice is an irritant and produces a burning sensation on skin contact and workers should therefore wear gloves while cutting the plant.

Ground up and dried, blacks use it as an ingredient in snuff and the Tswana in particular use a decoction as a purgative and a diuretic.

A fermented, intoxicating drink, 'pulque', is made from the leaf juice in Mexico.

The leaf contains strong fibres which, when pounded and washed in a river, can be twisted into strong ropes; the Zulus use them to tie up grass bundles.

The agave thus has a great many uses and should perhaps grow in everyone's garden. Even the root yields saponin and is used by some rural black people for washing clothes. A sugar, 'agavose', can be extracted from the flowers and leaves, and a peeled, softened leaf can be used as an external application to burns or contusions for quick relief.

ROOIBOS

Aspalanthus linearis

The rooibos was traditionally used by the Bushmen and Hottentots and botanist Carl Thunberg became interested in its uses in 1772 when he visited the Cape. It grows wild, mainly in the Western Cape and on the slopes of the Cedarberg, in sandy, non-acid soil. Commercial exploitation of rooibos tea began early in the twentieth century. Rooibos plantations are replaced every 6 or 7 years and it has gradually become evident that the benefits of rooibos are becoming world renowned.

Traditionally rooibos is best known for its use in allergic disorders. It is so full of nourishment that it can replace milk in milk allergic babies and is helpful in vomiting, diarrhoea and gastric complaints.

It is best drunk with lemon and honey, no milk. The Afrikaners, however, let it brew all day on the side of the stove and only then do they drink it and often with milk and sugar. A local farmer told me I did not know how to make 'Boeretee'. He instructed me to make a pot at five in the morning and to leave it simmering on the stove until 9 a.m. The first cup should be taken for breakfast after the cattle had been dipped. Then, at 11 a.m. another cup was refreshing and so on at intervals throughout the day, topping the pot with water every now and then! The best cup of all, with honey, was after dinner or just before bed, when the brew was so strong the teaspoon could almost stand up in it!

Long, long ago the Capoid people, who inhabited the Cedarberg, were the first to discover the exceptional qualities of the rooibos. During the summer they gathered the tea on the mountain slopes and prepared the stalks by chopping and crushing them with a wooden mallet and then drying them in the sun. The dried tea would fetch a good price. In 1904 Benjamin Ginsberg began marketing rooibos tea. During the thirties Dr L Nortier, a physician from Clanwilliam, realising the potential of rooibos tea, encouraged intensive cultivation through assiduous collection, distribution and treatment of the seeds.

In 1948 the Clanwilliam Co-operative Tea Company was established and flourished and, in conjunction with Benjamin Ginsberg, the marketing of rooibos tea was intensified. Today the company's warehouses and buildings cover over an acre of ground and the Rooibos Tea Board of Control has its offices there.

Not only is rooibos tea a healthy tonic tea but, given to children who suffer from hayfever or to babies with colic, it is a sure cure. In fact it can be used in so many, many ways that no home in South Africa should ever be without it.

Cold rooibos tea is a perfect base for a fruit punch.

PUNCH

30 ml rooibos tea
2 litres boiling water
250 ml honey
1 litre fresh orange juice
2 litres ginger ale

Pour boiling water over the tea leaves. Simmer for 10 minutes and strain. Dissolve honey in the hot tea and cool. Add orange juice and ginger ale just before serving. Garnish with mint leaves and crushed ice.

HERB TEAS

Rooibos as a base for herb teas, 3 teaspoons per pot.
Mint – Add mint leaves, a handful per teapot, to rooibos tea. Serve cold with brown sugar.
Peppermint – A handful per teapot, served hot with honey, is perfect for sore throats and
          colds.
Lemon Balm – Again a handful of leaves per teapot. Serve either hot or cold with brown
          sugar or honey for relief of headaches and fatigue.

ROOIBOS GINGERBEER

30 ml rooibos tea
1,5 litres boiling water
600 g brown sugar
15 ml powdered ginger
10 ml dried yeast
75 g raisins
1,5 litres cold water

Simmer tea in boiling water for 10 minutes. Strain. Add all ingredients, first mixing the yeast with a little warm water. Pour into jars but do not cover too tightly. Refrigerate after 12 hours. The gingerbeer is then ready to drink and is delightfully bubbly.

GINGER TIPSY TART

250 g dates
5 ml bicarbonate of soda
250 ml rooibos tea
115 g butter
200 g brown sugar
2 large eggs or 3 small
250 g flour
5 ml baking powder
90 g chopped walnuts or pecan nuts
30 ml chopped cherries

1 Fleabane (Erigeron canadensis)
2 Shepherd's purse (Capsella bursa-pastoris)
3 Dandelion (Taraxacum officinale)
4 Birdseed (Lepidium africanum)

1

2

3

4

4

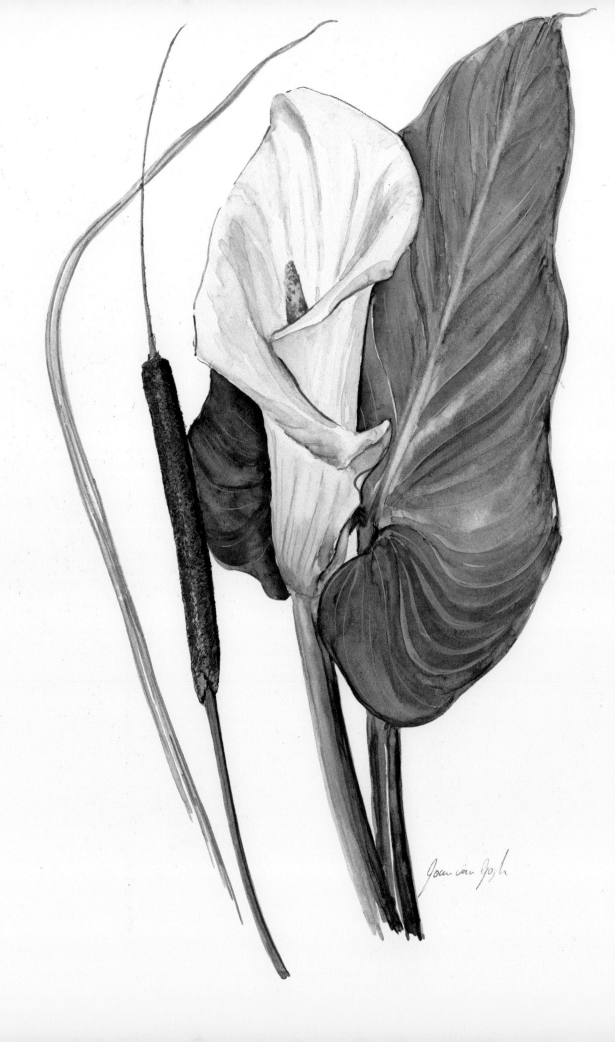

SYRUP

200 g brown sugar
250 ml water
15 ml ground ginger
15 ml butter
125 ml brandy

Pour hot tea over the bicarbonate of soda and the chopped dates. Cream butter and sugar, then add the eggs. Add the sifted dry ingredients, chopped fruit and nuts and the date mixture alternately to the creamed mixture.
Pour into a greased baking dish and bake at 180°–200°C for 40 minutes.
Boil up the syrup and pour over the cooling tart. Serve with whipped cream either as a pudding or as a teatime treat.

ROOIBOS TEA ASPIC

30 ml gelatine
30 ml apple cider vinegar
30 ml lemon juice
250 ml boiling water
1 chicken stock cube
15 ml brown sugar
250 ml strong, cold rooibos tea

Soak gelatine in the vinegar and lemon juice. Dissolve chicken cube in the boiling water, add to the gelatine and stir well. Add sugar. Finally add the cold tea. Stir well and then pour over cold chopped ham and hardboiled eggs, cold roast chicken pieces, cold sliced mutton or cold sliced potatoes, sliced hardboiled eggs and chopped onions. Serve with a green salad.

CAPE TOMATO BREDIE

75 ml oil
10 ml paprika
4 sliced onions
1,5 kg cubed mutton
6 large tomatoes
1 beef extract cube
250 ml strong rooibos tea
10 ml salt
1 clove garlic, crushed and chopped
pepper
30 ml chopped parsley
rice

Sauté the onions in the oil and paprika. Add meat and brown. Add chopped tomatoes and all the other ingredients. Simmer for about one hour or until the meat is tender. Add a little water if necessary. Serve with chopped parsley on a bed of rice.

Arum lily (Zantedeschia aethiopica)

FAT HEN
Chenopodium album

Goosefoot, Varkbossie, Sehelele (TSWANA)

This succulent wild spinach grows wherever the earth has been disturbed. Fat hen is closely related to Good King Henry (*Chenopodium bonus-henricus*) and the plant was eaten from Neolithic times until the present day. The fatty seeds were found to be included in the last meal eaten by the Iron Age 'Tollund Man' whose perfectly preserved body was discovered in a Danish peat bog in 1950.

The seeds, which contain fat and albumen, can be ground into a flour and made into a gruel to be used as a base for soups and stews. The leaves and seeds make a favourite nutritious poultry food and, as it grows prolifically almost the whole year round (except in mid-winter), it is a constant source of delight and makes a delicious fresh dish which is easily prepared.

Fat hen has many uses. The dried flowering plant can substitute for the fresh in the heart of winter. It is rich in iron, calcium and vitamins B and C. When used as a dye-plant, it produces a rich golden-red dye. Cattle seem to eat it freely although some tribes believe too much is poisonous to their stock.

The Zulus use the finely powdered leaf as a dusting powder to allay irritation about the external genitalia of children.

The Tswana make a spinach-like dish of fat hen at least once a week 'to keep the blood pure and the stomach working well'.

All the children on our farm gather great armfuls of fat hen from the mealielands and then sit in the shade of the thorntrees picking off the leaves, which wilt quickly. The leaves are plunged into a pot of salted boiling water and brought to the boil. The water is then poured off and the leaves are transferred to a fresh pot of water. Then a chopped onion or a handful of chopped spring onions is added, together with a little more salt and sometimes a few chopped potatoes. The mixture is then allowed to simmer gently until ready to be eaten.

Fresh leaves of fat hen rubbed into the hands soothes rough, dried skin and heals scratches.

FAT HEN CROQUETTES

500 g fat hen leaves, cooked
250 g mashed potatoes
salt and pepper
1 egg, beaten
breadcrumbs
chopped parsley

28

Chop fat hen and mix in with the potatoes. Chill for 15 minutes in the deep freeze, then shape into croquettes, dip in the beaten egg and roll in breadcrumbs. Fry in hot fat until golden brown. Serve sprinkled with parsley.

FAT HEN EGG DISH (serves 4)

500 g fat hen leaves, cooked
4 eggs
600 ml white sauce with cheese
breadcrumbs
salt and pepper
butter

Drain and chop up the fat hen, season to taste and dot with butter. Cover the bottom of an ovenproof dish with the fat hen, make hollows in four places and break the eggs into the hollows.
Pour the white sauce over, sprinkle with more grated cheese and breadcrumbs, dot with butter and bake at 180° for 20 minutes until the top is golden and the eggs are set.
Serve with a tomato and cucumber salad.

BUCHU
Barosma betulina

Introduced by the Hottentots, buchu is South Africa's best known herb. Buchu preparations have been used for almost every disease which afflicts mankind, but its greatest reputation derives from its use in kidney and urinary tract diseases. Local application to bruises and rheumatic pains has proved beneficial and the leaves have also been used in a bath for the relief of rheumatism.

Buchu brandy and buchu vinegar are both well-known tonics, and buchu can also be used as a liniment or embrocation. A small wineglassful is an excellent remedy for colic and stomach gripes.

Buchu leaves have a peppermint-rosemary type of odour and they are widely used in teas and drinks. The herb is now actually being cultivated in South Africa as its medicinal properties are arousing much interest throughout the world.

The flowers have a strong, sweet scent and are a lovely addition to a wildflower pot-pourri. The leaves dry well and are dotted with oil glands and when added to pot-pourri give off a wonderful fresh smell.

There is a South African herbal wine which is gaining popularity both here and overseas. This is made from a sweet white wine, to which 1% extract of buchu and 15% extract of *Artemisia affra* (wilde als) is added. A wineglassful taken daily is said to be of benefit in all digestive, kidney and rheumatic complaints.

The Hottentots apply the word 'buchu' to any herb that they find suitable for a dusting powder. They grind the dried leaves finely and use the powder as we would use talcum powder.

YARROW

Achillea millefolium

From ancient times, *Achillea* or yarrow has been used as a wound healer and to stop bleeding. Achilles was said to have healed his wounds and those of his soldiers by using the leaves and flowers of this herb and so gave it its name of Achillea.

It is also a wonderful herb for reducing fevers owing to its power of dilating the pores of the skin and producing copious sweating. It has been used as a substitute for quinine in the treatment of malaria.

Yarrow has proved beneficial in the treatment of so many illnesses and afflictions that no garden should ever be without it. It is still being used, with excellent results, in the treatment of hypertension and coronary thrombosis. Its astringent properties are effective for treating profuse menstruation.

For earache a salve can be made by melting cold cream and working in finely chopped flowers and a few leaves. A little beeswax can be added if necessary to help it solidify. A wad of this concoction is placed behind the ear and a rolled leaf, moistened and warmed, can be put into the ear, as well as a few drops of yarrow brew. Chewing yarrow leaves also helps relieve toothache.

To wash wounds and ulcers, use a strong, warm brew. To bring down a fever give the patient a yarrow bath as well as yarrow tea sweetened with a little honey.

Yarrow is also excellent for colds, diarrhoea, dysentery and for hysteria and epilepsy. It is also a proven aid in checking falling hair, for which a yarrow brew should be rubbed into the scalp daily.

Yarrow makes an excellent douche for female ailments and it can also be taken internally. Warm yarrow tea is soothing in cases of pneumonia, pleurisy, rheumatism and sore throats. The dosage is a handful of leaves and flowers to 1 litre of boiling water. Allow to steep for 10 minutes, then strain and sweeten with honey. A wineglassful taken morning and night should be sufficient.

An infusion of flowers is an excellent skin cleanser, as well as a tea to be taken at intervals in the day as a diuretic to help in a slimming programme and is ideal for cramp sufferers.

Yarrow planted near an ailing plant will restore it to health and keep all the neighbouring plants disease-free. It also seems to deepen the fragrance of the aromatic plants growing near it.

It is a quick and easy application to minor cuts and scratches, healing and stopping bleeding immediately.

A few handfuls of yarrow in the bath will do much to relax and soothe after a strenuous day's activities, and a face-pack made of the flowers is a quick beauty aid for a greasy skin. Some African tribes use dried yarrow leaves as a snuff for colds and bronchitis. A lotion made from the leaves is used for piles.

PARSLEY

Petroselinum crispum

No herb garden or vegetable patch is complete without a few parsley plants. Parsley belongs to the *Umbelliferae* family and there are several varieties, although the moss-curled parsley still seems to be the one favoured for garnishing and cooking in most English-speaking countries of the world.

Even the dried stems have their use – they make a green dye and were once extensively used to dye mohair and linen.

Chew fresh parsley leaves to sweeten the breath after eating onions or garlic. Parsley tea, also made from fresh leaves, is a wonderful treatment for kidney and bladder infections and flatulence and can also be used as a slimming aid.

Many people believe parsley is an effective treatment for rheumatism, a cup of parsley tea being taken daily with beneficial results. Parsley also stimulates the appetite and is therefore a wonderful addition to an invalid's diet, or for elderly people who find it difficult to eat.

Parsley is useful in treating most female complaints, such as cystitis, kidney infections, excessive and painful menstruation, while a strong brew provides an excellent tea for diabetics.

When weaning an infant, parsley leaves worn around the breasts inside the brassiere will help dry up the milk. Bruised leaves, steeped in vinegar, will relieve painful swollen breasts.

Warmed leaves and seeds will relieve insect stings and a lotion made of leaves and seeds and rubbed into the scalp will remove dandruff, stimulate hair growth, check baldness and remove lice!

Parsley is gaining recognition in the treatment of cancer and many herbalists have recommended the eating of parsley as a preventative measure in families which have a history of cancer.

In jaundice, rickets and anaemia, arthritis and sciatica, parsley is one of the most effective herbs and a handful of leaves should be eaten daily and a strong tea drunk twice daily. The dosage is a handful of leaves to 2 cups of boiling water, cooled and strained.

Parsley is well known as a garnish and can be used in soups and stews. Chopped parsley can be sprinkled onto vegetables and salads and mixed into cream cheese. Add it to cooked vegetables and stews just before serving as it is ideally at its best raw and uncooked.

Grown near roses and tomatoes, parsley is a wonderful companion plant, lessening the need for spraying to keep the roses and tomato plants insect- and disease-free.

32

MISTLETOE

Viscum capense, Viscum verrucosum

Cape Mistletoe, Voëllym, Martak

White people in South Africa use the juice of the mistletoe to rub on warts. In the early days in the Cape Colony it was used to treat epilepsy, St Vitus's Dance, and cure asthma. It was taken either as a decoction or as a powder.

Even today there are many people who still use it for asthma and bronchitis or to regulate menstruation. An infusion of the fruit is also used to stop haemorrhaging, especially nosebleeds. Mistletoe, however, is poisonous and therefore must be used with care.

The Zulus use a Viscum species in milk and administer this as an enema to children with stomach troubles, while the Xhosas use one of the Viscum species to treat lumbago and sore throats!

In times of drought the farmers cut down mistletoe to feed their cattle and, in spite of the astringency of the plant, the cattle seem to relish it.

In the Magaliesberg mistletoe is perhaps best known for the making of bird-lime and the Tswana children are particularly adept at this!

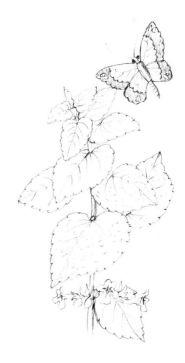

RUE

Ruta graveolens

Wynruit, Wynryk, Herb of Grace, Herb of Repentance

A remarkable plant, rue was once found in gardens everywhere as its medicinal values are so varied that no household was without a bush.

Twigs of rue were used in religious ceremonies; they were dipped into Holy Water which would be sprinkled about the church during Mass – this is possibly where the name 'Herb of Repentance' comes from.

In South Africa a decoction of the leaves is used in treating typhoid fever and scarlet fever. The juice of the leaf is also used to treat epilepsy and fits and convulsions in children. Putting bunches of leaves in the bathwater is said to prevent convulsions.

Blacks use a rolled up, bruised leaf packed into a hollow tooth to relieve toothache and the same treatment is found to relieve earache as well.

In the Transvaal crushed rue leaf and honey is still used as a respiratory and cardiac treatment, and a decoction of the bruised leaf is used in the treatment of jaundice and also to ease birth pains.

The Tswana drink a decoction of the whole plant during childbirth and also to ease menstruation pains.

Rue may be used to treat boils, abscesses and suppurating sores. Mix together two handfuls each of rue, chamomile, wormwood and 6 bay leaves. Boil for twenty minutes in a covered pan in a litre of water. Cool and allow to steep overnight. Reheat the brew and dip pieces of flannel into it, binding them firmly over the affected area. Change the flannel for a new piece dipped in the hot brew every 10 minutes. Repeat this six times and again in the evening. Use clean pieces of flannel each time and apply them as hot as can be tolerated. This is also very helpful for muscular aches and sprains.

The strong disagreeable odour and its acrid juice make one wary of the uses of rue, however. Rue can cause an allergy reaction on sensitive skins. Before treatment take a few rue leaves and rub a small area on the inner surface of the arm to test for allergy. If there is no reaction in 10 minutes, proceed.

The rutin the rue contains is believed to strengthen the will and even now, in southern France a bottle of country wine can be bought with a sprig of rue inside it, for the rue would not allow the wine to affect the body and cause drunkenness!

A rue decoction can be taken to relieve tiredness and stress, debility and anxiety, eyestrain, congestion, dizziness, palpitations and rheumatism of the hands and feet.

Rue is also a wonderful insecticide sprinkled on insect infested plants. Twigs of rue in the dogs' kennel will get rid of fleas and powdered rue is a good disinfectant. Bunches of rue hung up in the cattle stalls or in milking sheds will help combat flies.

Rue and basil cannot grow together; one or the other will die. Rue planted near

34

1 Nasturtium *(Tropaeolum majus)*
2 Watercress *(Nasturtium officinale)*

1

2

peach trees or in rows of tomatoes does much to deter fruit-flies and beetles. Twigs of rue placed around strawberries are a sure worm repellent.

The roots of rue produce a beautiful red dye.

1 Pretoriabossie *(Sida rhombifolia)*
2 Wild spinach *(Amaranthus caudatus)*
3 Bladder hibiscus *(Hibiscus trionum)*
4 Mistletoe

PRICKLY PEAR

Opuntia vulgaris

Turksvy

Various prickly pear species were originally introduced to South Africa from Australia and they grow easily in Africa's similar climate. In the Eastern Cape they have almost become a pest.

There is something very satisfying about growing so large a plant as this by simply placing a leaf in the ground and waiting, watching it send down roots and, in a few years, become an enormous, decorative addition to the garden.

The prickly pear grows wild all over the Magaliesberg and when my children were small the herdboys would bring them wire baskets packed with juicy prickly pears in the early summer mornings. They would all sit in a circle in the long grass and laboriously roll and rub and clean the fruit in the dew-wet grass.

Preparing the fruit is a marvellous experience. You start by cutting a sharp stick with a penknife to act as a fork and, holding the fruit firmly, cut off both ends and slit the side so that the cool, sweet, dripping fruit emerges from its pale green and pink cocoon. Piercing the fruit on the stick, it is pure delight to sit in that dewy grass and nibble at it. Big bites spoil the elusive taste; you should take your time if you want to savour it fully.

The fruit pulp is green, or orange or red in some varieties, but the taste is almost the same. A delicious prickly pear syrup can be made, but my favourite way of eating it is chopped up and served with whipped cream and a sprinkling of brown sugar, chilled and fresh – a perfect end to the summer supper.

The Xhosas and Mpondos make a beer known as 'iqilika ye tolofiya' from the prickly pear as the fruit ferments easily.

Both blacks and whites use the pulped leaf as a poultice for boils, suppurating sores and inflamed areas.

In the Transvaal a whooping cough remedy is made by boiling a leaf in 1,25 litres water for half an hour. The resulting liquid, strained, is then boiled with 250 – 375 ml brown sugar. Then, according to the age of the ill child, a teaspoon to a dessertspoon is given every half hour to one hour. A year old child should be given 1 teaspoon, 2 year olds 2 teaspoons, and 3 year olds 3½ teaspoons. From 4 years and upwards 1 dessertspoon is given.

A decoction of the leaf is used as a diabetes remedy, and for this a wineglassful of a strong decoction, to which a pinch of sodium bicarbonate has been added, is taken three times a day. The variety *Opuntia inermis* seems to be the best one for this purpose. Another method of preparation is to cover the minced leaf with sodium bicarbonate overnight. The black syrup that exudes may be used for diabetes but it will not effect a cure.

The prickly pear is an indispensable famine food and in times of drought has proved a life-saver to cattle, pigs and sheep, as well as the ostrich. At times our Afri-kaner cattle seek it out in the winter as the leaf stores quantities of water and winter grazing is very dry. The thorns of the very spiny varieties should first be removed before using as a stockfeed.

The prickly pear is also a source of fibre. A hundred tons of the plant yields one ton of paper pulp.

A chopped leaf thrown into a pool helps control mosquito larvae as the oil from the leaf floats on top of the water.

Sometimes one finds a prickly pear plant covered with the cochineal bug. From the time my children discovered this and saw the vivid red colouring ooze from a squashed bug, they never again wanted cochineal pink colouring in their cake icing!

At the end of the Christmas holidays the children and the herdboys gather the fruit daily and eat their fill as the season is very short. What cannot be consumed is turned into preserves to be spread on toast in the winter.

PRICKLY PEAR PRESERVE

For every 500 g peeled ripe fruit:
500 g sugar and 500 ml water.

Boil the syrup and slowly add the fruit, as well as 2-3 slices of lemon, without the pips, to every 500 g fruit. Boil rapidly until the fruit is transparent. Remove lemon rind and pack into hot bottles. Pour syrup over the fruit and seal.

DANDELION

Taraxacum officinale

Everyone is familiar with dandelions. The name 'dande-lion', the teeth of the lion, refers to the pointed, serrated edges of the leaves, so similar to the pointed sharp lions' teeth, and these same leaves included in your daily salad will strengthen the enamel on your teeth!

The leaves are full of vitamins and minerals, and dandelion leaves eaten as part of a salad are effective against obesity, useful in the treatment of diabetes, and will help to overcome exhaustion. The milky juice from the stems and leaves is an effective application for warts and blisters and should be applied daily.

Dandelion coffee can be made from the succulent tap roots. Wash and scrape the roots and set them in a low oven to dry out for about eight hours. Then pound and grind to a fine powder and use as a coffee substitute. Mix with a little real coffee to improve the taste and you will find it makes a pleasant drink.

Large doses of the leaf or coffee are purgative and diuretic, so care should be taken not to include too much in the salad or the after dinner drink!

Dandelion has also been used in the treatment of jaundice and liver ailments. The diluted milky juice makes an effective eyedrop for red sore eyes.

The bitter principle in the leaves and roots is due to the presence of taraxacin, a bitter crystalline substance, so the leaves should be used very sparingly in a salad.

EUCALYPTUS

Bloekomboom, Bluegum, Australian Gum Tree

All species of eucalyptus yield a volatile oil known as oil of eucalyptus and the percentage of oil varies from tree to tree and from species to species.

In South Africa eucalyptus oil has long been used as a cold remedy and as an ingredient in nasal drops. It is also effective as an insect repellent oil and as a rub for strained, sprained muscles.

The Zulus burn the green leaves to repel insects and a sprig put onto a fire during a braaivleis will clear the air and hastily put mosquitoes and flies to flight.

Bunches of eucalyptus leaves in the house during the winter, changed for fresh ones weekly, will keep the air from drying out and keep it smelling fresh.

Chopped green bluegum leaves spread near ants' nests will help to combat their tenacity.

It is not generally known that eucalyptus oil is poisonous, the symptoms in man being pallor, cyanosis, vomiting, rigors, cold sweat, dizziness and impaired breathing. It can be fatal. Remember therefore that the oil cannot be taken internally unless carefully prescribed by a homoeopath or doctor.

CATNIP
Nepeta cataria

Cats love catnip leaves and will eat them and roll in them ecstatically. Catnip is an ancient herbal medicine and is especially good for babies and young children for expelling wind, curing hiccups, calming and soothing. It is also wonderful for relieving colic and stomach cramps.

It is an excellent nerve soothing tonic for young and old alike. For children with bedwetting problems a sprig of catnip the size of an adult's thumb, combined with a thumb-sized sprig of marjoram, steeped in half a cup of boiling water and sweetened with a teaspoon of honey, given nightly just before the child goes to sleep, will do much to help.

Catnip is useful in the relief of pain associated with digestion and menstruation. A teaspoon of a standard brew – 2 thumb-sized sprigs to one cup of boiling water – taken before meals will help expel gas and aid digestion.

MARJORAM
Origanum vulgare

The word 'marjoram' means 'joy of the mountain'. Its aromatic oil is highly tonic and is beneficial to both man and animals. It is used in flavouring savoury dishes and is also an effective aid to digestion.

To chew a sprig of marjoram is one way of helping sour stomach fermentation and dispelling bad breath. It will soothe a sore throat, too, and ease a cough and is also helpful in morning sickness.

It is a calming and soothing herb and, combined with catnip, can help prevent bedwetting and stave off nightmares in children.

Marjoram is also beneficial in fevers, jaundice, rheumatism and headaches. A brew made with 2 thumb-sized sprigs per cup of boiling water is a standard one.

Externally, a few drops of warmed brew will help soften wax in the ears.

Marjoram tea is also an anti-depressant and taken daily it will alleviate anxiety, stress and depression.

CELERY

Apium graveolens

Seldery

This well-known table vegetable has medicinal uses too. Apiol is the oil found in its leaves and this gives the celery plant its strong pungent scent.

Celery is a wonderful prevention and cure for all rheumatic ailments, tumours and neuralgia. It helps remove stomach gas and will also restore a flagging appetite. It is thus often included in an invalid's diet in the form of a tea. As the whole plant is used, 1 dessertspoon per cup of either chopped leaves or stems, or 1 teaspoon of seeds per cup of boiling water, is the usual dosage. It should be taken three times daily. Divide the cup into thirds and cover the remainder or keep in the refrigerator. Make a fresh brew every day.

Celery should be eaten raw daily if you suffer from rheumatism, arthritis, neuralgia, sciatica, high blood pressure or liver ailments, including jaundice. It is also said to improve the eyesight and steady the nerves.

Ground celery seeds can be substituted for salt in salt-free diets, and celery seed tea is a useful diuretic. The seed is rich in natural soda and is therefore a good tonic.

CELERY HEALTH SOUP

Chop 4 large celery heads, stalks and leaves with 3 onions and a clove of garlic. Cover with water and boil. Add 45 ml parsley. As soon as it is cooked (about 15 minutes) put through a liquidizer and serve either hot or chilled. No salt is needed and this is a valuable soup for slimmers. Bon appetit!

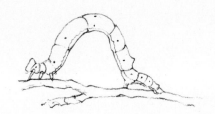

42

1 Basil (*Ocymum basilicum*)
2 Borage (*Borage officinalis*)
3 Thyme (*Thymus vulgaris*)
4 Sage (*Salvia officinalis*)
5 Lemon thyme (*Thymus citriodorus*)
6 Rosemary (*Rosmarinus officinalis*)
7 Lemon mint (*Melissa officinalis*)

SPRING

Granadilla *(Passiflora edulis)*

WISTERIA

Wisteria sinensis

Chinese Wisteria

Wisteria is commonly grown in South Africa as an ornamental plant, either as a creeper or pruned and trained as a standard shrub.

At one time the leaf was apparently used as a tea substitute but there is very little known about this practice. The bark yields a poisonous resin and a poisonous glucoside called wistarin, both of which, when ingested, induce vomiting, diarrhoea and finally a collapse.

The flowers in spring are a glorious sight and range from deep mauve to a white flowered type. Great binding stems of the deep mauve flowering wisteria literally hold our old farmhouse together and in spring the swathes of headily scented flowers stir the senses and the soul to almost painful heights. As the blooming period is so short, a mere handful of days, this makes it all the more special.

The flowers are followed by thick leaf growth, giving welcome shade, and in the autumn the leaves turn a brilliant yellow and then drop off in the first frosts, leaving silvery, twining stems that are also most attractive.

Wisteria vines, twisted or coiled and held in place with pegs or a twist of wire while green and young, grow into fascinating shapes by the winter and these can be cut and used in flower arrangements and decorations.

WISTERIA AND VIOLET POT-POURRI

Pick sprays of wisteria just before they are fully open and dry in the shade.
4 parts wisteria flowers and buds
1 part violet flowers
$1/8$ – $1/4$ parts crushed orris root
violet essential oil
$1/4$ part crushed lemon leaves and peel

Mix well and leave to mature in a covered crock for one month. Fill bowls and sachets with the mixture and place about the house, reviving from time to time with violet oil. This is a particularly soothing pot-pourri in a bedroom and if used during the winter months, placed on a warm windowsill or in front of a fire, the room is splendidly refreshed with a spring fragrance.

VIOLET
Viola odorata

Growing under the trees in spring and early summer, the clear purple flowers of the violet provide a startling patch of colour.

We pick the flowers for use in the pot-pourris and every year make a small special violet pot-pourri which is so highly perfumed it lasts indefinitely. It is easy to make:

10 cups violets
1 cup powdered orris root
½ cup rock salt
30 drops violet oil

Combine all the ingredients in a large screwtop jar. Shake daily, keeping the jar in a dark place. After a month place in a glass bowl with a lid. I use a disc of glass cut to the size of the glass bowl as the pot-pourri is so strong you cannot leave it open all the time. The violets do lose their colour so I constantly add a few dried violets to keep the pot-pourri attractive. It is advisable to open the bowl daily for a short time and stir the contents.

Blacks use violet leaves as a cancer remedy. They chew the leaves and also use crushed leaves as a poultice for skin cancer and growths, binding them over the affected part.

An infusion of the leaves is used for stomach complaints and a leaf dipped in water is a perfect dressing for burns.

Some of the 'old people' used the chopped root as an expectorant and purgative.

Violet flowers can be made into a strong tea and a teaspoonful may be given to infants as a mild purgative. A syrup can also be made of the flowers and used as a nerve tonic for children.

Violet leaves are also used for the drawing of boils and abscesses and a macerated leaf held over a bad pimple with a band-aid or sticky plaster at night will heal it quickly.

A few leaves in a salad are good for soothing the nerves and calming restlessness. A tea will have the same effect made with a few leaves and flowers and sipped with honey. This will do much to ease tension and a tension headache in particular. Five violet flowers eaten, followed one hour later by another three, will soothe a headache.

CRYSTALLISED VIOLETS

This is a delicious sweetmeat and crystallised violets are most decorative on iced cakes or on cream puddings.

Make a syrup of 500 g sugar and 225 ml water. Boil for five minutes. Drop the violets into this syrup and boil for 1 minute. Using a slotted spoon, lift the violets out of the syrup and place them on a tray lined with greaseproof paper. If it is necessary to rearrange the petals, do so at this stage (using tweezers is easiest). Leave the tray in a warm, dry place for about 3 days, until the violets are completely dry and hard. Store in a glass jar with a well-fitting lid.

HONEY OF VIOLETS

This is a really unusual delicacy and an unfailing success when served with hot buttered scones for morning tea.
250 ml water
500 g honey
180 g violet flowers

Boil the water and pour over the violets. Leave to stand, covered, for 12 hours. Then add the honey and boil for about 30 minutes until thickened. Pour into hot, clean jars and seal.

VIOLET ICE-CREAM

1 litre fresh cream
250 g icing sugar
violet colouring
3 whipped eggs
crystallised violets to decorate
2 bunches (about 3 cups) violet flowers

Remove the green calyx from the violets. Heat the cream and infuse the violets in it. Leave until cold, then whip the cream and add the icing sugar. Fold the beaten eggs into the cream and sugar mixture. Add a very little violet colouring and freeze. Decorate with crystallised violets.

MULBERRY

Morus nigra

Once, long ago, the mulberry was an important medicinal plant and of course its leaves were used for the feeding of silkworms for the silk industry.

The fruit contains sugar and malic acid, pectin, vitamin C and the fruit, leaves and bark are nutritive and anti-pyretic.

In the Balkans the leaves were until recently employed in treating diabetes and in Europe the bark was at one time used to remove tapeworms.

The fruit gives a deep purple dye but this can be removed by rubbing the stained fabric with green fruit. It was once used to dye medicines.

Delicious drinks and jams can be made from the fruit.

MULBERRY DRINK

Pick and clean a basketful of fruit. Place the fruit in a pot, pour in just enough water to cover, and add sugar to taste. I weigh the fruit, then add half the weight in sugar. Bring to the boil and leave to stand until cool. Strain the fruit through a metal sieve, bottle and keep in the refrigerator. Dilute with soda water and serve with ice and a sprig of mint.

MULBERRY JAM

Weigh equal quantities of fruit and sugar. Place the fruit in a heavy-bottomed pot, add a small amount of water, just enough to cover the bottom of the pot, and put onto a slow heat. Bring to the boil, stirring frequently. Simmer until it thickens (about 1½ hours). Spoon into hot sterilised bottles, seal and store. Serve as a jam or as an accompaniment to vanilla ice-cream.

PERIWINKLES

Vinca major, Vinca minor

Periwinkles grow equally well in shade or sun and will cover a bank quickly. The star-like, mauve-blue flowers may be used as an astringent. Place about twenty flowers in a bowl of rainwater in the sunshine. Leave for several hours, then bottle and use for rinsing the face after washing in soapy water.

A standard brew made from a handful of leaves and flowers is also a wonderful calming tea. Sweeten with honey.

Long strands with the flowers on them, submerged in motor car anti-freeze fluid in a shallow bowl, will turn a glorious brown and become soft and supple. They can be used over and over again in flower arrangements. The anti-freeze compound has the same effect as glycerine and water, and the leaves and stems absorb the fluid.

The periwinkle is used for nose-bleeds and internal and external haemorrhages. It dries up wounds and sores and can also be used as a nerve tonic as well as for allaying chronic diarrhoea.

The standard brew is: 250 ml flowers and leaves to 1 litre boiling water. Allow to stand for 10 minutes, then strain and drink one wineglassful 3 times a day.

SPRING AND SUMMER

ROSE

Rosa

No flower on earth has had more written about it than the rose. Universally loved and esteemed for its beauty and fragrance, it has held so warm a place in man's heart for centuries that it has come to mean almost more than any other flower. It has a great many and varied uses.

Rose perfume is a favourite fragrance and the perfume industry from the early centuries has been primarily involved with roses.

Rosewater can be easily made early in summer and is most useful for flavouring and for cosmetics. Pick a basketful of fragrant roses (my favourite is Crimson Glory). Pack into a large pot with sufficient water to cover them when they are well pressed down. Bring to the boil and add more rose petals. Once the water has boiled, remove from the stove and leave covered overnight. Next morning strain off the beautiful red liquid, discard the petals and bottle. If it is a large quantity, keep the bottled rosewater in the refrigerator.

One bonus is that every time you make rosewater or rose petal wine, the entire house is locked in a cloud of heavenly rose perfume. Sometimes when I am expecting a number of visitors at the studio and herb garden, I set a copper pan of rose petals in a little water at the side of the stove and guests are enchanted by the glorious rose fragrance.

Long ago rose decoctions were used for headaches, pain in the eyes, sore throats and to fix the teeth in the gums. Powdered roses in wine were believed to cure 'women's ailments'. Brews were made to cure falling sickness, weak memory, jaundice and scars on the skin. There never was such a panacea and whole industries were based on the growing of roses for medicinal purposes, as varied as they were numerous.

Rose hips, full of vitamin C, can be made into jellies, drinks and syrups. In the autumn it is an enjoyable task to gather the red and orange hips and pound them into a colourful mass.

ROSE HIP JELLY

Pick a basketful of rose hips. Wash well and trim. Chop and pound them and place in a pot with just enough water to cover them. Boil until soft. Strain through cheesecloth overnight.

To every 500 ml liquid, add 350 g white sugar. Boil rapidly until setting point is reached. Bottle and seal in hot sterilized bottles.

1 Honeysuckle *(Lonicera periclymenum)*
2 St John's wort *(Hypericum perforatum)*

9

1

2

10

1

2

ROSE PETAL CONSERVE

Pick 100 red, strongly scented roses (I use Crimson Glory). Heel them by cutting off the small whitish triangle at the base of each petal. This part is bitter so be sure to remove all the white parts.
juice of 6 lemons
3 kg white sugar
2,5 litres water

First boil the sugar and water, then add the rose petals. Boil briskly for one hour. Add the lemon juice. Boil until the syrup becomes thicker (about another twenty minutes), spoon into hot sterilized jars, and seal with wax when cool. Serve on thin slices of white toast spread with butter and experience an unusual taste – the conserve tastes like the smell of red roses.
The conserve can also be served with vanilla ice-cream or with a milk pudding.

ROSE ICE-CREAM

500 ml heeled red roses
250 ml castor sugar
250 ml rose wine
500 ml thick cream
2 eggs, beaten well

Whisk cream and castor sugar. Liquidize the rose petals with the wine. Add the eggs, rose petals and wine mixture to the whipped cream mixture. Pour into ice-cream trays and freeze. Serve with pink rose petals all around the dish.

ROSE PETAL YOGHURT

10 red roses, heeled
500 ml plain yoghurt
honey to taste

Liquidize all the ingredients and serve chilled.

ROSE PETAL TART

300 g flour
45 ml sugar
3 ml salt
125 ml sunflower oil
45 ml water

Mix and knead and press out into a greased pie dish. Bake at 200°C for 15 minutes. Cool.

FILLING

500 ml cream
2 eggs, beaten
60 ml icing sugar

1 Calabash (Lagenaria siceraria)
2 Cosmos (Cosmos bipinnatus)

500 ml plain yoghurt
60 ml rosewater
6 red roses, heeled

Whip cream and icing sugar. Add eggs and yoghurt and whip well. Chop rose petals and add with the rosewater. Mix well. Pour into pastry case. Bake 190°C for ¾ hour, cool and refrigerate.

ARUM LILY

Zantedeschia aethiopica

The fresh leaf of the arum lily has been used for many years by all South African peoples as a dressing for boils and sores. The leaf should be warmed before applying. It is also soothing for insect bites.

The early Cape colonists used the same procedure for gout and rheumatism and for the treatment of wounds. The leaf acts like oiled silk over the wound, keeping out air and germs so that the healing process can carry on in ideal conditions.

The juice of the plant is an irritant and it is poisonous. Chewing even a tiny piece immediately makes the tongue and mucous membranes of the mouth and throat swell up. However, the Southern Sotho make a spring vegetable dish from the leaf and petiole. Boiling or roasting destroys the toxicity of the plant.

Arum lilies have been cultivated as a source of food for pigs from the time of the first colonists and, as they grow easily along swamps and streams throughout South Africa, it is easy to see that their food value was explored.

The flowers make a lovely indoor arrangement and often can be found growing throughout the winter under protective trees. They are extremely long lasting, cut or growing, and are a worthwhile addition to a shady, moist garden.

CORNFLOWER
Centaurea cyanus

Surely no garden is complete without the glorious royal blue cornflower. No other flower has this intense blue and a bowl of tightly bunched cornflowers on a kitchen table is a sure lifter of spirits.

The cornflower is an introduced 'weed' to South Africa and was once found abundantly growing over cornfields of Europe, annually seeding itself with vigour.

The blue flowers are effective as an eye-wash, and useful in chronic and acute inflammation of the eyes. Treatment even shows positive results with corneal ulcers. A brew, made from 50 flowerheads to 1 litre of water, is excellent for insect or scorpion bites and also for surface wounds and grazes.

Cornflowers make a wonderful tonic tea, sweetened with honey and a lemon slice added, for nervous debility and indigestion. Except for the narrow leaves, all parts of the plant have a renet-like enzyme and the flowers have a beautiful blue dye for natural fibres.

Dried flowers add charm to pot-pourri mixtures although they have no scent. Sprinkled on top of a spring pot-pourri and covered with a glass lid, they are most attractive.

SPRING POT-POURRI

2 parts jasmine flowers
1 part orange blossom
½ part cornflowers
½ part jonquils or narcissus
¼ part powdered orris root
jasmine oil

Mix the jasmine, narcissus, jonquils and orange blossom. Seal. Add the jasmine oil to the orris root and seal for one week. Then mix the dried flowers with the orris root-oil combination and leave sealed for a further week. Finally, place in glass jars with the blue cornflowers sprinkled on the top. Keep sealed and revive with jasmine oil from time to time.

HONEYSUCKLE

Lonicera periclymenum

The whole honeysuckle plant is medicinal. It is good for the heart, good for rheumatism and arthritis, good for skin disorders and wounds and is also a beautiful, fragrant ingredient in pot-pourris, sachets and pillows.

An ancient asthma remedy which is still effective today is:
A handful of flowers, well crushed, mixed with sufficient honey and molasses (equal parts) to bind the flowers. The dosage is 1 tablespoon of the confection to be eaten morning and night.

The crushed leaves are a good wound healer when warmed in hot water and applied to wounds, sores and ulcers.

A handful of flowers made into a tea and sipped early in the morning to ease a sore throat is a sure remedy and this same brew is excellent for rheumatism and stiffness of the joints, as well as arthritis.

The bees love the honeysuckle and honey from its flowers is quite delicious.

We grow honeysuckle everywhere on our farm. It covers fences, and is a good binder of the soil and is thus excellent for ground cover on slopes. It makes good shade-houses and arbours.

Bowls of trailing flowering stalks in the house last long enough to make the entire house headily fragrant.

The pink variety is perhaps better in pot-pourris as it is more fragrant, if that is possible, and the pink flowers seem to retain their perfume longer when dried.

MIDSUMMER HONEYSUCKLE POT-POURRI

4 parts honeysuckle flowers
2 parts pinks (or clove carnations)
2 parts moss rose petals (pink)
¼ part powdered orris root
¼ part crushed cinnamon sticks
few drops rose oil or carnation oil

Combine the ingredients and keep covered until the winter. Then, in the cool months, place open bowls in the bedrooms and the summer scents will fill the air. Revive periodically with rose or carnation oil.

MUSTARD
Brassica nigra

Mustard is so easily cultivated that it should find a place in every garden. The leaves are hot and biting and make a tasty addition to salads and soups.

The whole plant is an important antiseptic tonic and is used in the treatment of flatulence, poor appetite, colds, catarrh and pneumonia. Externally it is used as a poultice or rub for inflammations, rheumatic and arthritic pains and stiffness as well as for congested lungs.

When a cold is threatening, a few mustard seeds chewed several times during the day will dispel the mucous that accumulates. A handful of leaves in a salad will soothe a cold and generally cleanse the blood.

To make a mustard plaster, mix a handful of crushed seeds with a handful of wholewheat flour into a paste, using hot water. Add 2 tablespoons of vinegar. Spread on a cloth and apply hot over the area to be treated, eg the chest, kidneys or arthritic joints. In cases where the skin is sensitive, add the beaten white of an egg to the mixture.

Gathering your own mustard seed and grinding it into a paste, adding cider vinegar and a little honey, is infinitely satisfying and it is so delicious served with grilled meats and fish that you will find that no shop-bought mustard can ever compete for flavour and richness.

When my children were small they each had their own mustard garden which they cultivated on the kitchen windowsill and which was the start of their interest in growing things.

Line a flat baking tray with a double layer of lint or cottonwool. Water well and sprinkle mustard seeds evenly over the surface. Within a few days the seeds will sprout and shortly thereafter bright green leaves appear. Be sure to keep the cottonwool wet and when the little plants are a few centimetres high cut them with kitchen scissors. They are delicious on sandwiches and sprinkled over roast chicken. The next tray can be started as soon as the leaves appear.

MAIDENHAIR FERN

Adiantum capillus-veneris

The beautiful common maidenhair fern, which makes an excellent houseplant, has been used medicinally for many centuries. The plant was found growing prolifically throughout Britain and central and southern Europe. It has since been naturalised in many other parts of the world where it is still used for chest complaints, respiratory catarrh and pleurisy.

The leaf, when boiled with sugar and water, forms a syrup called 'capillaire' and in the nineteenth century it was the preferred drink of the 'young ladies'. Dr Johnson, according to Boswell, flavoured his port with a dash of capillaire. Capillaire was once a popular cough syrup and was in constant demand.

Maidenhair grows easily indoors and out and can be found growing wild in shady positions along the furrows and banks of the Magaliesberg rivers. The generic name *Adiantum* is from the Greek word 'adiantos', meaning unwetted, for the leaf repels water, and its natural habitat is a wet environment.

The Southern Sotho smoke the dried leaf for head and chest colds and the Zulus make a tea which is almost jelly-like it is so mucilaginous, also for chest colds. During Victorian times and still used today, the sugared leaf makes an attractive decoration for iced cakes and puddings. The leaf in any bouquet is beautiful and will last a long time if the bottom half-inch of the stem is burned.

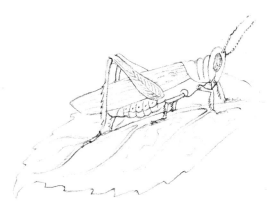

ASPARAGUS

Asparagus officinalis

Aspersie, Sparrowgrass

There is no other known herb that acts so powerfully on the urinary system as the asparagus plant. The tasty young shoots contain a unique crystalline principle called 'asparagin' and this is of benefit in all infections of kidneys and bladder and acts favourably on the lymphatic system. It is also used for the treatment of jaundice, dropsy and gallbladder infections.

A tea can be made of the fern and sweetened with honey. Taken morning and night it is beneficial for all of these ailments, as well as for heart disease, flatulence, rheumatism and chronic gout.

The water in which the young shoots have been boiled, although bitter, is said to be extremely beneficial for rheumatism.

Black people use the shoots and fern as a diuretic, a laxative and for their cardiac and sedative effects. There are several indigenous species and these are also believed to have the same properties.

Asparagus is grown as a commercial crop in South Africa, and the shoots are available fresh or canned.

The root and fruit, too, are considered a powerful diuretic and have been used successfully to treat bladder and kidney infections. In Europe a decoction made from the fruit was used as a contraceptive and also to induce menstruation.

Asparagus plumosus, which grows wild in the Magaliesberg, has been used in the treatment of pulmonary tuberculosis, and the fern-like leaf and the root for rheumatism and bladder and kidney infections.

In early spring the young green tip shoots should be gathered before the buck and the hares find them, cooked in boiling water (change the water twice while cooking) and served with melted butter for a glorious treat.

For medicinal purposes, the shoots should be eaten raw.

The Mpondo nursing mother keeps two pieces of asparagus root with her and nibbles a little of it each time she feeds her baby in case something bewitched may have been put on the path along which she had been walking!

One species of asparagus, known by the African name of mugarahanga-rukatu, grows on anthills, and is used to neutralize the effects of snake venom, as well as an aphrodisiac and a gonorrhoea remedy.

Young fresh shoots of either the cultivated or the wild asparagus, lightly boiled, cooled and chopped, added to salads, are a great favourite for everyone and in the spring and summer should be eaten as often as possible as a general tonic for the system.

1 Castor oil plant *(Ricinus communis)*
2 Ivy *(Hedera helix)*
3 Southernwood *(Artemisia arboratum)*

1

2

3

1

2

3

SPRING, SUMMER AND AUTUMN

1 Quince *(Pyrus cydonia)*
2 Bluegum
3 Agave *(Agave americana)*

SORREL

Rumex acetosa

Sour Dock, Suring, Bodilanyana (SOTHO)

In the Transvaal the leaves of the *Rumex acetosa* or sorrel are used in the treatment of abscesses.

Despite its high acid content, the leaf has also been used in Europe as a vegetable and as an antiscorbutic and was once used in the treatment of scurvy.

Chopped leaves added to salads and soups have a fresh pleasing flavour and they are a wonderful thirst quencher and may revive and refresh a weary walker in the heat of a summer day.

The leaf has been used as a poultice in acne and skin ailments and the Tswana chew the leaf and then apply it to sore spots and pimples on the face.

The root is used as a tonic and diuretic in both South Africa and in Europe and a decoction of the root and seeds is used as an astringent in diarrhoea. However, it is not suitable for old people or children.

There are contra-indications, however, as large doses are poisonous and will cause kidney damage. Cases have been reported of sorrel poisoning in sheep and cattle.

The herb should *not* be used by those suffering from rheumatism, gout, arthritis, kidney stones or gastric hyperacidity.

SORREL QUICHE

1 large bunch sorrel leaves
30 g butter
salt and pepper to taste
250 ml plain yoghurt
3 eggs
6 spring onions, chopped
baked pastry case

PASTRY

300 g flour
3 ml salt
125 ml maize oil
little water

Mix well and knead. Press into a large pie dish or two small dishes. Chop and wash the sorrel leaves, and cook in the butter with chopped onions. Beat the eggs and yoghurt. Add seasoning. Mix with sorrel and onions, pour into the pastry case and bake at 200°C for 20 minutes. The quiche can be served hot or cold.

DOCK

Rumex obtusifolius, Rumex crispus

Broadleaf Dock, Curled Dock, Ubuklunga (XHOSA), Idoloenkonyana (ZULU)

The dock is a close relative of the sorrel and has been used medicinally for many centuries. It is a native of Europe but is widely distributed in temperate and sub-tropical countries as a weed.

It contains, among other things, tannin, resins, salts, volatile oils, starches and thiamine. The combined actions of these are both astringent and purgative and dock is therefore used as a tonic laxative.

It is of much value in treating skin complaints, liver sluggishness and constipation.

The leaves may be applied to ringworm, scabies and urticaria and the powdered dried root is used in the treatment of laryngitis as a gargle, and as a mouthwash and tooth powder in gingivitis (the inflammation of the gums).

Black people use a decoction of dock in the treatment of anthrax, often combining it with *Teucrium africanum* (galbos or bitterbos).

The dried rhizome has a bitter, astringent taste and was once used as a blood purifier and in the treatment of skin diseases as well as a general tonic.

The young leaves can be eaten like spinach, but it is advisable to cook them in a change of water to get rid of the slightly bitter taste.

In the case of nettle stings, of course, dock is the universal treatment and it is also effective for other skin rashes and inflammations. The Tswana use warmed dock leaves as a comforting dressing for swollen breasts during lactation and they also use them for the treatment of piles, the leaves first being pounded and pulped.

In the olden days dock leaves were used to wrap butter when going to market. I remember as a child that a fresh dock leaf was always placed in the butter dish to keep the butter cool and fresh.

STUFFED DOCK LEAVES

12-18 leaves, blanched by pouring boiling water over them. Dry and brush both sides with olive oil.

STUFFING MIX

2 cups cooked rice
1 cup bacon chips
1 cup chopped mushrooms
½ cup chopped onion

Fry in a little oil and mix with a beaten egg and a cup of yoghurt, salt and pepper to taste. Place spoonfuls on the leaves, roll up and fix with a toothpick. Serve warmed.

SPEEDWELL

Veronica officinalis

A gentle, low-growing wild herb, speedwell grows everywhere. The leaves are tiny and serrated but the minute, beautiful blue flower irresistibly draws the eye. This little herb has wonderful healing properties seemingly out of all proportion to its size.

A tea made of the leaves and flowers and sweetened with honey is a soothing tonic to internal tissues and removes excess mucous from the body. The tea is made with 1 cup boiling water and 3 or 4 sprigs of speedwell (approximately thumb size). The tea can be used for coughs and bronchial asthma, tuberculosis, jaundice, dysentery, as an eye-wash for all eye ailments and to improve the eyesight. Cooled, it is excellent as a wash for ulcers and rashes.

Speedwell is fairly pleasant to eat in salads. I have found it growing lushly at the edges of pathways even in midwinter where it has had some water from the garden sprays.

In bygone days people would use speedwell as a spring tonic after winter coughs and colds. The tonic was made up of 250 ml speedwell leaves, flowers and stems, 500 ml boiling water, 1 sprig rosemary, 10 ml honey and juice of half a lemon. This was drunk daily first thing in the morning for at least a fortnight as the winter came to an end, and its benefit could be felt immediately.

CARROT
Daucus carota

The carrot is one of nature's most wonderful medicines. In South Africa it has long been used to treat diarrhoea in children and the old Afrikaner remedy for threadworm is to give 2 tablespoons of grated carrot first thing in the morning; this treatment can be carried out indefinitely, until the threadworms are eradicated.

Scrapings of the root are a beneficial dressing for ulcers and tumours, swellings and old wounds. A fresh poultice should be made twice daily and applied.

Grated raw carrot is used for kidney and bladder ailments. A tea can be made from the fresh leaves.

Grated raw carrot eaten daily gives relief from painful menstruation and it is also a remedy for jaundice and anaemia. Herbalists use the juice (from 500 ml up to 1,25 litres juice is drunk daily) in the treatment of cancer.

The carrot is rich in natural insulin and should therefore be included in the diet for the diabetic.

Although bitter, a few pieces of the leaves, finely chopped, should be added to the daily salad and a brew of the leaves, sweetened with honey, is excellent as a general tonic, for anaemia and all lymphatic ailments, and varicose veins. A small wine-glassful taken morning and night is sufficient.

There need be no specific dosage, but as much raw grated carrot as the body will tolerate, eaten daily, is of utmost importance in our diet to cure the above ailments and to keep us healthy and disease-free.

Chopped carrot leaves are an excellent addition to chicken and duck fodder and are a favourite with sheep, cows and pigs. However, if eaten in any quantity, they may taint the cows' milk!

SUMMER

WHEAT

Triticum agropyrum species

Sprouts are nutritive and a tonic for the whole body, and particularly good for anaemia. The bran, which is a gentle laxative, can also be used as a poultice. Fill a bowl with hot water, sprinkle in two handfuls of bran and use as a bath for skin ailments – rash, eczema, insect bites. Germinated seeds can be used in salads and in savoury mince dishes. Sprinkled on top of grilled steak or roasted chicken, sprouts are delicious.

A field of wheat is pure pleasure from its midwinter sowing time when the brilliant green spikes show above the dark, tilled earth until the warmer weather approaches when it grows more brilliantly emerald in a landscape of buffs and browns.

The monkeys come down from the mountain and, with the baboons and the duikers and steenbokke, eat their fill of winter salad. By spring, the wheat ears are formed enough to gather bunches. Together with Iceland poppies in a huge copper bowl, there is no arrangement that lifts the soul quite as much as this truly country pleasure.

By October the wheat has turned golden and before the combines come, great sheaths are quickly bundled together to be used in baskets and crocks for the summer and autumn as decoration in the house. I make little sprays to give away as a symbol of friendship in the year until the next crop is sown.

1 Violet *(Viola odorata)*
2 Rock rose *(Cistus villosus)*
3 Soapwort *(Saponaria officinalis)*
4 Vinca rosea *(Lochneara rosea)*

1

2

Joan van Gogh

MELISSA

Melissa officinalis

Bee Balm, Lemon Mint

Melissa is the sweetest of all herbs and bees in particular love it. It was introduced into Britain by the Romans.

It is effective for nervous troubles, can be used in surgical dressings, it calms the heart and, as Gerard claimed, 'driveth away heavyness of mind, sharpeneth the understanding and increaseth the memory'.

It is also excellent for polishing wooden furniture, by rubbing a handful of green leaves over the surface. The oil in the leaves is thirstily absorbed by the wood and the whole room retains a lemony fragrance for a long time afterwards.

Teas are made from the dried herb all the year round, but in summer melissa tea is a beautifully refreshing, cooling drink, sweetened with honey and served with slices of lemon and ice.

For a large jug, use 4 handfuls of melissa leaves. Pour boiling water over the leaves and leave to stand overnight. Next morning, strain off the pale green tea, sweeten to taste and refrigerate. Add the sliced lemon just before serving, together with a sprig or two of fresh herb in each glass. The tea may also be given to anyone who has been bitten by venomous insects or by a dog.

A few chopped melissa leaves in a salad are beneficial for tension and nervous disorders.

Sachets or bunches of melissa, hung in cupboards, help deter moths and keep linen fresh and sweet smelling.

1 Yarrow *(Achillea millefolium)*
2 Kweekgras *(Cynodon dactylon)*

KHAKIBOS

Tagetes minuata

Khakiweed, Mexican Marigold, Afrikanderbossie, Monkhane (SOTHO), Mbanje (NDEBELE)

This strongly aromatic annual is common throughout South Africa and takes over easily in the old lands, along the roadsides and waste places. Khakibos originally came from South America and is now firmly established in South Africa.

It is a wonderful insect repellent and the Tswana place branches of midsummer khakibos in amongst their blankets and winter clothing to repel moths and other insects. If the dogs' baskets and kennels are lined with khakibos, the fleas will soon leave and a few leaves rubbed into your pet's coat is a sure flea repellent.

Khakibos is gathered by the truckload in our area of the Magaliesberg and taken to a nearby processing plant where the oil is extracted for use in the perfume industry. The resultant concentrate has a surprisingly pleasant perfume and is exported to France as a fixative.

In the winter months, after the first frosts, the dried seed-heads are headily fragrant but have lost their sharp, burning scent. These should be gathered to use as a fixative in moth-repelling sachets. Combined with other herbs, the mixture has a pleasant eau-de-cologne type fragrance and is most useful placed into small bags and put into cupboards and drawers to keep them insect-free.

INSECT REPELLENT SACHETS

1 part lavender leaves and flowers
1 part eau-de-cologne mint
1 part wormwood
1 part santolina (cotton lavender)
1 part khakibos seed-heads
1 part crushed dried lemon peel
few drops oil of lavender
½ part crushed coriander seeds
¼ part cloves

Mix ingredients together, add the oil of lavender and leave sealed for 2 weeks, shaking daily. Fill cotton bags with the mixture and tie with ribbons. Place in all cupboards and drawers throughout the house. Crush the bags from time to time to release the fragrance.

Between rows of calabashes, pumpkins, tomatoes and melons, plant khakibos thickly. It is a marvellous pumpkin fly repellent. To shade the ripening fruits, I cut khakibos from the edges of the fields and cover the fruit with it, powdering a few leaves around the area as well. You will find, as I do, that there will be no need to spray.

When tomatoes are ripening and some of the lower fruit hangs close to the ground, a bed of cut khakibos will protect the heavy fruit from insects and prevent soft, wet patches forming where it touches the ground.

Cucumbers seem to love the shade of khakibos over them and they grow beautifully under their strongly scented roof in the midsummer heat. Khakibos on the compost heap seems to discourage cutworms and ants.

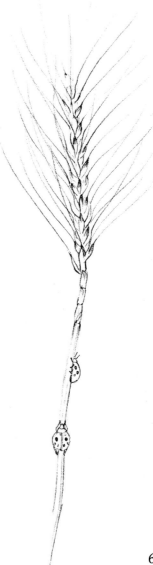

69

PRETORIABOSSIE

Sida rhombifolia

Queensland Hemp, Taaiman, Ivivane (SWAZI)

The tough pretoriabossie reaches a height of one metre at times and, as it grows so easily and is so common, it deserves a mention.

In Europe it has been and still is regarded as a valuable remedy for pulmonary tuberculosis, rheumatism and snakebite.

In India it is used in the form of an infusion for tuberculosis and rheumatism, while in Central Africa the root is used as an abortifacient and the leaf as a poultice for inflammations.

The Tswana sometimes use the tips of the stems, the new young leaves and buds, as a purgative if other favourite herbs are not available. The 'old people' sometimes used it as a diarrhoea remedy – 'to clean out the body'.

The most valuable use of the plant, however, is its strong white lustrous fibre content! Fibre from Swaziland and the Pretoria area is particularly good in length and strength.

The seed capsule is believed by some to be poisonous but it seems to grow vigorously in all the chicken runs on my farm and the chickens are perfectly healthy. Sida is virtually indestructible and has to be forcibly pulled out of the ground.

The Tswana pull out a tall plant growing near the river and break or tear off the side branches. Then, laying it on a rock, they pound the thick stem with stones. The tough fibres soften after being washed in the river and, when twisted, it becomes a strong, useful rope used to bind the bundles of firewood or sticks they carry home on their heads.

PURSLANE

Portulaca oleracea

Purslane is an annual which grows wild everywhere. The Tswana gather basketsful after the rains from the mealie lands. After stripping the leaves from the pink, fleshy stems, and rinsing the leaves in cold water, these are placed in a pot on the stove, adding only the juice of a lemon and a sprinkling of salt.

The cooking time is very quick but the mixture should be stirred constantly. Serve either as a green vegetable with a few dabs of butter and salt and pepper, or mashed into sweet potatoes with a little sugar and butter.

As a cold summer salad with chopped cucumber, lettuce and mint, purslane is delicious. Here again, strip the young leaves from the stems and add to the salad, with an oil and lemon juice dressing.

In the sixteenth century it was widely cultivated as a valued pot herb and was excellent then, as now, for blood disorders, fevers and high blood pressure, headaches, anaemia and diabetes.

A handful of leaves in a salad is a must.

COMFREY

Symphytum officinale

Knitbone

Comfrey grows wild in Europe and has been introduced into Africa where it is becoming more and more important as an animal feed. It has received much attention in recent years both as a medicinal plant and as a source of protein and the research into its potential continues.

Comfrey was once the main herb used in the treatment of fractures. It contains an active principle, allantoin, which aids in healing and the pounded root forms a mucilaginous mass which can be bound over the fracture; as it dries it hardens and helps to hold the bone in place.

The root and leaf are also used in the form of a tea for the treatment of pleurisy, bronchitis and pneumonia. A tablespoon of chopped leaves or pounded root to a cup of boiling water, strained and mixed with honey, should be given every 2 hours to bring relief. This same brew is also used in the treatment of duodenal ulcers and lesions, and for diarrhoea.

The pounded root, warmed in a little water, can be made into a poultice for wounds, severe bruises, skin eruptions, dermatitis, ulcers on the legs, varicose ulcers and swollen varicose veins. Eczema can be washed in a lotion made of the leaves and roots and an external poultice made of cloths soaked in a strong, warmed lotion and bound over the area is considered beneficial in rheumatism and neuralgia. Burns and sunburn respond quickly to comfrey cream or lotion.

There are records going back almost two thousand years of comfrey being used in herbal medicine. The ancient herbalists and healers had no knowledge of the vitamins, minerals and proteins which we now know comfrey contains, but they had ample proof of its amazing healing powers and it was widely used for many ailments.

Comfrey also makes a quick, excellent compost and comfrey fed to cattle suffering from mastitis is a sure cure.

Comfrey is a tasty vegetable and as it grows so easily, only dying down in winter, it should be included in our diet regularly.

COMFREY AU GRATIN

Cook sufficient young comfrey leaves and chop finely. Make a strong white sauce and mix with the comfrey. Cook the same quantity of brown rice. Spoon a layer of rice into an ovenproof dish, then a layer of comfrey in white sauce and a layer of grated cheese and so on, ending with a layer of cheese. Place under the grill for a few moments and serve piping hot.

COMFREY FRITTERS

Wash several young comfrey leaves, dip into batter, fry in oil and serve with salads.

BATTER

2 eggs
250 ml milk
10 ml baking powder
pinch salt
60 ml melted butter
500 ml flour

Beat eggs and mix into all other ingredients.

BODY BUILDING HERB SOUP

Comfrey should be included in this nutritious soup which is particularly beneficial for invalids and growing children.
Chop equal quantities of:

watercress
sow thistle
comfrey
celery or lovage
mustard greens
fat hen

Add chopped chives and a few chopped onions, green tops included. Grate into this a few carrots and one or two of the leaves. Cover with water and bring to the boil. Simmer slowly for half an hour. Salt to taste and finally add chopped parsley and serve hot with home-baked brown bread and butter.
The soup can be liquidized and served cold with a little cream added for a delicious summer meal.

SHEPHERD'S PURSE
Capsella bursa-pastoris

The astringent and antiseptic properties of shepherd's purse are out of all proportion with its insignificant appearance. It grows easily on waste ground and seeds itself readily. It gets its name from the seed capsules which resemble the old-fashioned sling purses the shepherds used to carry.

Perhaps its best use is as emergency first aid to stem heavy bleeding. A strong brew can be made of the whole herb. Use a heaped tablespoon to a cup of water and then drink 2 tablespoons three times daily, particularly in cases of nosebleeds and heavy menstruation.

The same brew is good for dysentery, diarrhoea and kidney infections. It can be used to wash out wounds. It can also be taken internally for earache, a teaspoon of the warmed brew being dropped into the ears and the base gently massaged.

Shepherd's purse is used in Europe as a malaria remedy and to lower blood pressure. It is an excellent tonic and a few leaves chopped into a salad gives it a pleasing peppery taste.

1 Fat hen *(Chenopodium album)*
2 Sunflower *(Helianthus annuus)*
3 Wilde als *(Artemisia affra)*

1

2

3

Joan van Gogh

16

1

2

3

Joan van Gogh

SWEET PEPPER

Capsicum annuum

Chilli Pepper, Red Pepper, African Chilli, Tabasco Pepper, Miripiri (SHONA)

All the capsicum species are originally of American origin and became known when the physician who sailed with Columbus on his second voyage in 1494 to the West Indies noted the use of capsicum by the natives.

Black people are very partial to all the capsicum varieties and the fruit is an important ingredient in Central African calming medicine.

In Hawaii the plant is believed to be antibacterial and is used as a remedy for rheumatism and pains in the back, as well as for swollen feet.

Internally the fruit acts as a stomachic and a condiment but excess can lead to stomach-ache and an inflammatory reaction on the mucous membrane of the stomach.

Blacks believe that capsicum is beneficial for liver and blood conditions and therefore it is often included in the diet.

The capsicum contains vitamin C and is considered nutritive and a stimulant, aiding digestion, and can be used fresh or dried with equally beneficial results.

The leaf was once used as a dressing for sores in the plague, and dried, powdered cayenne pepper is used by several African tribes as an insecticide.

The stuffed sweet or red or green pepper makes an appetising summer meal and, as the plants can be easily grown throughout the warm months, it is also a useful addition to summer salads.

1 Wild olive *(Olea africana)*
2 Blinkblaar *(Ziziphus mucronata)*
3 Traveller's joy *(Clematis virginica)*

PENNYROYAL

Mentha pulgium

Pudding Grass

The name 'pulgium' comes from the Latin for 'flea' – 'pulex' – and denotes the power of this plant as an insecticide.

It grows abundantly in the Cape Province and its high oil content makes it a valuable medicinal plant. It is highly toxic, however, and the use of the oil internally leads to irreversible kidney damage; great care must therefore be taken at all times.

Pennyroyal can be used for minor gastric disturbances in the form of a weak tea for flatulence, nausea and menstrual pain and, in combination with other herbs, it is used for the treatment of a head cold.

Once it was used to treat snakebites and dog bites and it is still used today as an effective insect repellent. When the leaves and stems are well pulped and rubbed onto the skin mosquitoes are quickly put to flight.

In the rainy season the Tswana women working in my herb garden pick handfuls of pennyroyal to take back to their homes in the evenings. They rub themselves and their bedding with the herb, and also their children and their dogs. They believe this ensures a good night's sleep.

As an effective treatment for catarrh and bronchitis, tuberculosis and 'female' complaints, such as irregular or suppressed menstruation, pennyroyal was at one time firmly believed in. The dosages were mild – a handful of leaves and stems to one litre of hot water, allowed to steep and then drunk, a wineglass at a time. This same brew was an excellent inhalation to clear the sinuses. Pennyroyal should, however, only be used under medical supervision.

A handful of leaves and stems, crushed and inhaled, clears a stuffy nose and brings relief to blocked sinuses and often effectively relieves a headache.

The plant dies down in winter but quickly spreads and flowers in early summer. The dried stems and leaves are very effective in moth repelling sachets and added to pot-pourris give a fresh and pleasing scent.

When the summer flies are a nuisance in the kitchen I gather a basketful of pennyroyal, crush it and rub it along the windowsill and counter tops and leave a bowlful here and there. The flies soon disappear.

MORNING GLORY

Ipomoea purpurea

Purperwinde, Ijalamu or Injalambu (ZULU)

The twining, binding tendrils and stems of the common morning glory are considered a pest in most gardens and in the mealie lands. This species is native to tropical and sub-tropical America and has often been cultivated and then allowed to run wild in other countries.

The root and stem of the morning glory are used by the Zulus as a purgative and as an anti-syphilitic. The active principle in the stem is resin and it also contains a volatile oil and a fraction of a percent of potassium chloride and nitrate. This is why it is an effective purgative.

The pleasure gained from fences, gates and walls covered in morning glory of a summer morning is so constant that no South African can fail to appreciate it and one almost forgives the nuisance value of the bindweeds.

Some of the 'old people' used a brew of the flowers and stems as a tonic and cleanser of the blood and found morning glory helpful in dropsy, but it is seldom used nowadays.

CHICKWEED
Stellaria media

Starflower, Qoqobala (SOTHO)

Chickweed is a common garden weed everywhere. The seed is used as food for caged birds and chickens love its fresh greenness. It tastes good eaten in salads too, and its healing properties are useful for the digestive system, chest conditions, skin ailments and for all eye conditions.

Stellaria comes from the Latin meaning 'star' and this herb, too, has been used medicinally from ancient times. It grows prolifically and readily seeds itself so that it can be found virtually all the year round in warm areas of South Africa.

A brew can be made of the leaves and stems and used externally for skin and eye eruptions.

The whole plant, washed and gently crushed, can be applied to sores or ulcers, held in place with a bandage. Change the plant every three hours and apply a fresh one. It will draw out all impurities from the area.

Chickweed is used homoeopathically in the treatment of rheumatism and should also be eaten daily in a salad while under treatment.

It is a soother of the digestive tract and is excellent for ulcers and indigestion and can also be taken in the form of a tea. For this, use one small handful of chickweed to one cup boiling water.

In South Africa chickweed has been used by whites and blacks alike for the treatment of haemorrhoids, blood diseases, eczema and eye ailments and is useful as a medicinal bath. Use four handfuls of the herb, pour 4 litres of boiling water over it, allow to steep and cool and use to wash skin ailments, ulcers and wounds.

Chickweed is delicious in soups and stews when added within the final three minutes of cooking time. The Tswana gather the young shoots and make them into a type of spinach dish with the addition of potatoes and onions.

TUMBLEWEED

Boophane disticha

Candelabra Flower, Gifbol, Seeroogblom, Leshoma (TSWANA), Incwadi or Iswadi (XHOSA), Motlatsisa (SOTHO)

This beautiful plant, with its pincushion of red and pink flowers in early summer, although poisonous, has such a variety of uses, for blacks in particular and to some extent whites too, that it had to find a place in these pages.

The bulb, with its dry scale layers, is used by the Xhosas as an application to boils and abscesses and as an outer dressing after circumcision. They also use it in the treatment of redwater for cattle.

In the Cape some whites still today use the scale of the bulb to draw out pus from whitlows, boils and abscesses and septic sores. It is also considered a good pain reliever when bound over the infected area or over rheumatic areas and bruises.

The Swazis chew the bulb's charred outer layers into a type of pitch from which they fashion the headring or headdress worn by the chief and headman.

Several tribes believe that growing the plant outside their huts will ward off evil spirits and bring rain and good luck.

In the Karoo whites use a mattress filled with the bulb scales to combat sleeplessness and hysteria, but owing to its poisonous properties this practice should be undertaken with the utmost caution!

The Hottentots and Bushmen use a preparation of the bulb for poison arrows for shooting smaller game. They believe that a bulb grown in the shade is more toxic than one grown in the sun.

The above ground parts of the tumbleweed are apparently not poisonous as vultures and other carrion birds eat the leaves and top parts of the bulb either 'to prevent harm from the ingestion of putrid flesh or to sharpen their vision', as Burtt Davy suggests.

Black people make a decoction of the bulb as an enema for suicide, apparently, as an infusion of the bulb is toxic enough to cause a coma within a short while of drinking it.

Sniffing the flower and inhaling its pollen causes headache, giddiness and drowsiness so in all cases the tumbleweed should be approached warily.

The Xhosa and Sotho people apply the outer layers of the bulb for relief of pain from burns and as a treatment for skin rashes and urticaria. The scale is first moistened with water and then lightly bound over the area.

The dried leaf, moistened with either milk or oil, is used for the treatment of eczema and other skin diseases, as well as varicose ulcers, and many blacks today still believe the bulb will 'drive out' headaches, weakness and abdominal pains.

By Christmas time the dried seedhead tumbles across the veld and open grasslands in the wind. When driving along the farm roads one often finds the tumbleweed caught up in a fence.

When hung on nylon fishing line, tumbleweed heads make lovely indoor decorations. For Christmas, glue dried wild flowers onto the terminal spikes and tuck little sprays of dried white baby's breath (*Gypsophila elegans* or *Statice latifolia*) in amongst the 'spokes'. The resulting delicate flower-ball hung over the Christmas table adds a fragile, delicate touch to the festivities in the hush of the summer heat.

LEMON VERBENA

Lippia citriodora, Aloysia triphylla

Lemon verbena was originally from South America and was introduced to Europe by the Spanish. The name Aloysia comes from the name Maria Louisa, wife of King Charles IV of Spain. Its use in the early days was to give a lemon scent to finger bowls at banquets.

It is a half-hardy shrub that needs wind and frost protection. It is cultivated in greenhouses and as an indoor shrub in Europe. On the Highveld it loses its leaves in winter and should be covered with grass or hessian in the frost. It can be easily propagated by woody cuttings in spring.

Its essential oil content makes it valuable in perfumery and it is a beautiful addition to pot-pourris, sachets and pillows.

The leaf may also be used in the form of a tea as an anti-spasmodic and is beneficial in the treatment of nausea, indigestion, flatulence and vertigo. The tea, made from dried leaves, is very relaxing after a big meal and can be added to freshly squeezed lemon drinks, sweetened with honey or brown sugar and served with ice and mint.

PEACE PILLOW

Equal quantities of:
red rose petals
lemon verbena
peppermint
lavender
¼ quantity of dried hops mixed together with:
⅛ part coarse salt
⅛ part crushed orris root
few drops lavender oil

These ingredients, blended and allowed to stand for one month in a sealed container, form the base for the peace pillow that brings sleep, tranquillity and peace. Foam chips can be added when stuffing the pillow to soften it. I use approximately 1 part of foam chips.

WINTER POT-POURRI
(To refresh smoky, stuffy air in the house)

lemon verbena
lemon peel
crushed cloves

orris root
yarrow
lavender
tansy
nutmeg
cinnamon
lavender oil

Stand in an open bowl on the hearth. Revive with lavender oil.

82

1 Khakibos *(Tagetes minuata)*
2 Sow thistle *(Sonchus olearceus)*
3 Blackjack *(Bidens pilosa)*
4 Common groundsel *(Senecio vulgaris)*

1

2

3

4

1

2

3

4

5

6

Joan van Gogh

WILD STRAWBERRY

Fragaria vesca

The wild strawberry makes a lovely dark green ground cover and its bright yellow flowers and red berries are a constant delight.

A few berries rubbed on the teeth will whiten them and freshen the mouth. A tea made from the leaves is good for diarrhoea, enteritis, dysentery and faulty menstruation. Thirty grams of the roots to 1 litre of water, boiled for 10 minutes, is prescribed for inflammatory conditions of the kidneys or bladder and the same decoction is used for gout, arthritis and jaundice. It should be mentioned that the brew sometimes reddens the stools and gives a pink colour to the urine.

An American doctor in the nineteenth century, Dr Blackburn, left a tried and tested remedy for dysentery. This consists of 375 g green wild strawberry leaves to 1,15 litres good spirits (brandy is usually used). Boil until the liquid is reduced to 550 ml, strain and administer the potion, 1 tablespoon every 3 hours, until the symptoms disappear. It usually takes 8 – 10 tablespoons to effect a cure.

The cultivated strawberry has similar properties, but the wild strawberry has a longer season and is richer in iron. Eat as many as possible in their short season and preserve some for the winter in melted honey with a little brandy added.

A brew of the leaves is excellent as a soothing lotion for eczema, sore eyes and styes on the eyelids, migraines and headaches.

The strawberry, being such a wonderful cleanser, is useful in all blood disorders, lowered vitality and lack of appetite and should be cultivated in gardens everywhere.

Matthiolus, four centuries ago, said of the strawberry: 'It seemed good to me to receive this joyous and profitable plant into the bourgeoisie of my garden and so speak of it as follows: the leaves and the root cause to urinate and greatly serve the spleen: the decoction of the root, taken as a drink helpeth inflammations of the liver and cleanses the kidneys and the bladder: the juice of the fruit cureth blotches on the face.'

WILD STRAWBERRY JELLY

1 kg wild strawberries
juice of 3 lemons
500 ml water
sugar

Boil the strawberries with lemon juice and water. Simmer for 10 minutes. Strain through a jelly bag and measure the juice. Add 300 g sugar to every 500 ml juice. Dissolve over low heat, then boil briskly until setting point is reached. Ladle into hot, sterilized jars and seal.

1 Russian tarragon *(Artemisia dracunculoides)*
2 Field bindweed *(Convolvulus arvensis)*
3 Chickweed *(Stellaria media)*
4 Buchu *(Barosma betulina)*
5 Cleavers *(Galium aparine)*
6 Asparagus *(Asparagus officinalis)*

GARDEN STRAWBERRY ICE-CREAM

1 kg hulled strawberries
1 litre thick cream, whisked
1 tin condensed milk
juice of 2 lemons
little castor sugar sprinkled on the strawberries

Mash the strawberries with a fork, leaving a few whole to decorate when serving the ice-cream. Whip the condensed milk and lemon juice. Add to the whisked cream. Finally add the crushed strawberries, lightly beaten with a fork, into the cream mixture.
Pour into freezer trays and freeze overnight. Serve garnished with strawberries and strawberry leaves.

84

PEPPERMINT

Mentha piperita

A favourite fresh and invigorating tea can be made from peppermint leaves. It helps combat sleeplessness and relieves indigestion. It cleanses and strengthens generally and is excellent for over-excitement, shock, cramps and heartburn.

It grows well in the shade but is happy in the sun too. Branches hung in the kitchen along with sweet basil are effective in keeping flies away.

Peppermint is one of those glorious 'cure-alls' that leaves you feeling fresh and clean. Its uses are many – for flatulence, wind, gripes and stomach-aches. A cup of hot tea, sweetened with honey and sipped slowly, while inhaling the steam, will relieve even the most stubborn headache.

It is good for relief from painful menstruation, mental depression, inducing sleep, reviving spirits, curing fainting attacks and constipation – a mixed bag indeed.

PEPPERMINT PILLOWS

2 parts pennyroyal
2 parts peppermint geranium
4 parts black peppermint

Mix together. Add a few drops of peppermint oil and either stuff a little pillow or keep in a wide, shallow bowl beside the bed, covered in the daytime and uncovered at night.

MIDSUMMER PEPPERMINT PUNCH

Make a large pot of peppermint tea, using 2 good handfuls to a large teapot. Allow to cool. Pour off liquid.
Add the juice of 10 oranges. Sweeten with honey or brown sugar. Refrigerate and serve with ice chips in long glasses. Garnish with a sprig of fresh peppermint.

This recipe can also be frozen to make ice lollies. The children make it in the hot Christmas holidays in individual lolly moulds and it is such a favourite with all ages that a fresh batch is made daily. It really does cool one down and is most refreshing.

PEPPERMINT FACIAL STEAM TREATMENT

In the heat of the summer this is a particularly refreshing end-of-day reviver.
A handful of peppermint leaves is brought to the boil in an open enamel pot of water. I always use rainwater as it is a natural combination with herbs. Remove from the stove and hold the face over the pot and inhale the steam, using a towel tent over the head to minimise the loss of steam.

When no more steam is rising, the pot can be brought to the boil for a second time and the procedure repeated. Afterwards, the face should be washed in clear, cold water. This is also wonderful for hayfever and coughs and colds. The inhaled fumes clear the nose beautifully.

MAIZE

Zea mays

Mealie, Mielie, Umbila (SWAZI), Mavhele (VENDA), Imome (ZULU), Poone (SOTHO)

The most widely grown of the summer crops, maize forms the staple diet for blacks. It is the only known cereal which can sustain life for man and animals over a long period without any other foods. Maize contains a rich oil as well as vitamins, minerals and starch.

The leaves around the cob and the inner 'silk' are all medicinal. The inner leaves, bound over wounds and sores on humans and animals alike, promote healing and draw out all offensive matter.

The silk is used for kidney and bladder ailments and as a diuretic and for all ailments of the prostate gland. The silk can be eaten raw, chopped into mealie-meal porridge, or it can be made into a tea, 2 tablespoons fresh silk and 1 tablespoon dried silk simmered in 1 cup boiling water for a few minutes. Drink a cup in the morning and another in the evening.

Marewu is a thin, soured porridge made from ground mealies and much loved by black people.

The most healthy way to eat mealies is off the young, fresh and raw cob. Lightly cooked, then spread with butter and sprinkled with salt is the method favoured by most white South Africans.

The maize oil is extracted from the seeds and used in the manufacture of soap and paint. It is the chief raw material in artificial rubber. Maize oil is excellent as a hair tonic and for the treatment of eczema of the scalp.

The mealie husk is used in paper making and the centre of the cob, from which the mealies have been separated, is used for the manufacture of celluloid, the base from which linoleum is prepared.

The leaves and stalks are used as cattle fodder and the dried cob makes a useful cork. The cobs are burned on the tobacco seed beds in the winter after the crop has been harvested and has gone through the combine. The ash of the burned cobs forms a base for the Swati snuff.

Living on a mealie farm, it is natural to become totally involved in the seasons affecting the crop. The ploughing and fertilizing of the lands must be completed after the first spring rains and planting must be completed in our area by mid-December. Then come the green rows of young mealies and a watchful, anxious eye is kept on the blue summer skies. Rain is needed, but hail is not welcome.

At Christmas time, from the early planted rows in the vegetable garden, the first cobs are ready to be picked, plunged into the pot and, in the cool of the evening those perfect, tender young cobs, dripping butter, are relished by all.

In January and February the problems of heat and drought are always critical –

will the plants come through? Sometimes the flowering stalk withers and dies before pollination.

With autumn come the swelling cobs, bringing much activity to the kitchen with the making and freezing of green mealie bread and mealie puddings for the winter.

Then it is winter, with the frosts, and the dry leaves and cobs can be heard rustling in the wind. Lovely sunny days are spent gathering the cobs, the crackle and snap and the gentle chat of the Tswana men the only sounds as they walk slowly up and down picking the cobs and filling the sacks. The heap of bleached white husks grows, the roar of the threshing machine fills the air, the load of bags filled to the brim is stacked high on the trailer and the putt-putt-putt of the slowly moving tractor pulling its heavy load fades away in the cold shadows of the winter evening. Then the shouts of activity as the last bags are stacked in the sheds and the men hasten home to their firesides.

As the first sun touches the white blankets of frost on the yellow grass, so the next day begins, picking, loading, thrashing, loading bags of seed and stacking them in the farmhouse sheds. There is something so peaceful about gathering in the crop in the golden sunlight in spite of all the hard work. A picnic basket left under the thorntree at the edge of the land holds a thermos of hot tea, a tin of buttermilk rusks and huge, juicy midwinter navel oranges – a feast fit for a king to refresh one midmorning.

Attractive 'flowers' can be fashioned from the beautiful, almost white inner husks. Petal shapes can be cut, placed in warm water to make them pliable and fastened with thin florist's wire around a dried seed pod to make unusual decorations.

Every winter without fail I string together a bunch of golden mealies, husks turned back, to hang in the kitchen. If the mealies are sprayed or dipped into an insect killer, they will last indefinitely and we gather and bunch great quantities each winter for the 'town ladies' who want a little bit of country in their kitchens.

GREEN MEALIE BREAD

6 green mealies, cooked
2 eggs, whisked
2 rounded teaspoons sugar (10 ml)
3 ml salt
10 ml baking powder

Slice the mealies off the cobs and mince them. Mix other ingredients and blend with the mealies. If the mixture is too stiff add a little milk, enough to make a soft dough. Place in a greased bowl, tie tinfoil over the top and steam for 2 hours. Slice and spread with butter.

NASTURTIUM

Tropaeolum majus

The nasturtium is a living green antibiotic! The common garden nasturtium derives its name from the Greek 'tropaion' which means 'trophy' because the flower and leaf evoke the helmet and shield of the trophies with which their monuments were decorated.

Elizabeth Christine, daughter of the Swedish botanist Linne, was the first to observe that at dusk on a hot summer's day sparks were emitted from the heart of the flower, causing scientists to turn their attention to the chemical composition of the plant. This strange phenomenon was discovered to be connected with the high phosphoric content of the nasturtium.

The nasturtium is used in the treatment of the urinary tract, in cystitis and for inflammation of the kidneys, as well as an application for chronic sores. The leaves and juices from the stems are bound over the affected part and left overnight.

It is used in chronic bronchitis, bronchial catarrh and emphysema. Infuse 2 – 3 g fresh leaves in 100 ml boiling water for 5 minutes. Strain and drink a sherry glass of the liquid two or three times a day.

The seeds or fruits can be pickled like capers. Pack the seeds into a bottle with a sprig of thyme, a few cloves and 2 bay leaves. Cover with hot apple cider vinegar and a sprinkling of salt. Seal and store for a month before use.

An excellent treatment for colic or digestive gripings is a teaspoon of nasturtium seeds, ground and given in enough water to liquify, every three hours.

A poultice of seeds, crushed and placed on a bandage, then wrung out in hot water, may be used on boils, abscesses, styes and old sores that have not healed. This done twice daily is an effective treatment.

In the treatment of worms in children, give the child six to ten green seeds to eat first thing in the morning (ie on an empty stomach) for three days.

A few leaves and even the flowers included in a salad are a wonderful cure for nervous depression, tiredness and poor eyesight.

If you have a sore throat immediately eat 3 nasturtium leaves, and then again 2 at intervals of 3 hours, until the throat is healed.

Slices of sweetmilk cheese wrapped in nasturtium leaves is a favourite family snack in my household and tastes especially good when eaten on the beach!

JOB'S TEARS

Coix lacryma-jobi

Traangras, Coixgras, Tandegras, Ilozisi (ZULU)

This grass, with its bead-like seeds or glumes, is regarded as a precious acquisition and is found from Africa to China, Brazil to India and even further afield.

The Zulus place a necklace of the seeds around the neck of an infant, with the idea of warding off teething troubles and the grey beads are given to the baby to chew upon in the form of a bracelet or necklace.

In the Philippines the seeds are made into rosaries, necklaces and bead curtains, as well as trays, bags and other decorative objects.

A beer can also be made from the semi-ripe seeds, which is both nourishing and pleasant. In Europe a decoction of the seeds has been made and used for centuries for catarrhal infections and bronchitis.

The Chinese use the seeds in kidney and bladder infections and for rheumatic conditions. In Malaya a decoction of the root is used as a vermifuge in children and a flour made from the ground seeds is used for treating dysentery.

In Japan, the East Indies and Brazil the seed is considered a nutritious food and it is ground into a flour. The feasibility of introducing coix flour into Brazil to replace wheat flour has been explored, as Brazil has to import her wheat but can grow coix easily.

Some of the old Zulus used the juice of the stalk to rub into itchy bites or stings but they do not find it so effective nowadays, and this remedy is all but forgotten.

Job's tears makes an interesting summer crop and the heads or plumes, when picked before they ripen fully, and then dried, make an attractive decoration in a copper bowl.

To have the seeds in the house is considered extremely lucky and a necklace will protect the wearer from misfortune!

1 Cornflower *(Centaurea cyanus)*
2 Sorrel *(Rumex acetosa)*
3 Dock *(Rumex crispus)*
4 Speedwell *(Veronica officinalis)*

1

2

3

4

1

2

3

Joan van Gogh

WANDERING JEW

Commelina

There are two types of commelinas that grow equally easily over large areas of the country. They seem to thrive in shade or in the sun and tend to take over wherever ground has been cleared for crops.

The yellow-flowered *Commelina africana* is used by the Zulus as an infusion to bathe a restless child and the leaves rubbed over the sleeping place of a restless sleeper is believed to induce calm.

The Southern Sotho crush and cook the leaves and root and combine it with other herbs as a medicine for a young woman who is barren. The ash of the plant is also used as one of the ingredients in an application to the loins to cure sterility.

The blue-flowered *Commelina beughalensis* is used for burns, the leaves crushed and the extracted juice applied to the painful area.

The leaf can be used as a vegetable but it can be laxative. The Tswana feed it to their pigs in times of food shortage.

The commelinas are most useful as ground covers in wild places and free-range hens seem to scratch happily amongst them.

In Mauritius the blue-flowered commelina is used as a suppository for an enema and is safe for babies. A thick piece of stalk is peeled, and the smooth glutinous sap makes it easy to insert.

The Tswana cook up the leaves with a small amount of water and use it for excessive menstruation and sometimes for bladder complaints.

On the compost heap the commelinas break down quickly and easily and as the seed germinates and spreads so easily, it is an effective way to get the compost heap productive.

1 Comfrey (*Symphytum officinale*)
2 Rue (*Ruta graveolens*)
3 Thorn apple (*Datura stramonium*)

91

PIG'S EAR

Cotyledon orbiculata, Cotyledon leucophylla

In many country gardens the pig's ear succulent is to be found as it is widely used as a medicine.

The leaf is scratched and pulped to extract the juice and this is applied to warts and corns, held in place with a sticky plaster for 14 nights. It is particularly effective for obstinate planter warts. The juice softens the corn so that it can be peeled off easily.

The heated leaf is also applied externally for earache, and the Xhosas use warmed drops of juice for inside the ear as well as for toothache.

The Southern Sotho use the dried leaf as a protective charm for an orphaned child; it is tied around the child's neck on a thin string.

Cotyledon leucophylla, found growing wild in the Magaliesberg in rock crevices, protected from the frosts, is used by the Tswana as a drawing poultice. The leaf is warmed in hot water and placed on accessible inflammations. This Transvaal species is poisonous and is easily confused with the Cape variety, *Cotyledon orbiculata*.

WILD PINEAPPLE

Euchomis undulata

Kxapumpu

In late summer sometimes we are lucky to find, in the grasslands, a lush tuft of 'kxa-pumpu'. It is a rare find as the local black people value this plant highly as an anti-witchcraft charm.

One can buy the wild pineapple from local nurseries and it is most attractive and unusual, but it does die down in the winter. In early summer a rosette of broad, elongated leaves is produced which spread out several feet in some cases. By February, a pale green, pineapple-shaped inflorescence appears.

The bulb is sometimes used as a remedy for abdominal pain and distention but local blacks use it as a remedy or restorative after excessive conviviality!

Kxapumpu is much used by the witchdoctor. He makes a decoction of the leaves and shavings of the bulb and washes himself with the resulting brew to protect himself from being bewitched. Our herdboy used the leaves effectively for 'gallsick-ness' in the cattle by giving the ailing cow a few leaves to eat amongst the grass and green lucerne.

BLACKJACK
Bidens pilosa

This is a pest in any garden but of great importance to the Zulus, who chew the young green shoots for relief of rheumatism.

A tea can be made of the leaves and young shoots for any inflammation, taken internally, and an infected wound can be washed out with the same tea.

After cattle have been grazing off young blackjack plants in early summer, their milk has a definite, fairly strong, unpleasant taste, but when mixed with hay and other green fodder, it is unnoticeable. Cattle will seek it out, as will hens and ducks, and chopped young plants quickly turn into a beautiful rich compost.

Our herdboy told us of his grandmother cooking the young leaves and shoots as a spinach. A little fat or oil is put into a pot over the fire and the chopped leaves are slowly added, with very little water added and a sprinkling of salt. Stirring continuously, the plant is soon cooked, but only the tips and tender leaves of the very young plant are used as the bigger leaves are bitter.

A tea of the flowers is made for colic and diarrhoea by the Tswana and the Zulus.

94

BUTTERCUP

Ranunculus multifidus

If you hold a buttercup under your chin and it shines on your skin, it means you like butter – a children's game!

I love the name 'rana' – a frog – and ranunculus is derived from this, as it grows in moist places. All along the furrows these brilliant yellow flowers shine in amongst the green growth and waterweeds. There seem to be two varieties growing on our farm, the usual straggly, tall form which I have found in shady, damp places up to half a metre in height, and a squat form with a few short-stalked flowers.

A tea can be made of the leaves and flowers to soothe coughs and sore throats. It is also effective for vomiting and diarrhoea.

A poultice of the leaves can be made by covering a bowlful of leaves with hot water. The hot, softened leaves are applied to the throat and swollen glands during a mumps attack. The Zulus also use this same application for treatment of cancer. The affected area is covered with the hot leaves and the treatment is repeated daily.

The Xhosas believe buttercups to be poisonous, but they do use a poultice of the leaves for various skin ailments, scabies and venereal sores.

In the Louis Trichardt area even today the ash of the plant is mixed with mutton fat and applied to the fontanelle of a baby to reduce fever.

Some of the Tswana in our area dry the plant and use the powdered leaves as snuff, but the young people neither use it nor like it.

BASIL

Ocymum basilicum

Basil has been cultivated for more than four thousand years. In India it is a perennial but in South Africa, in the Transvaal particularly, it is treated as a tender annual as it is the first plant to be frosted at the the start of winter.

There are many varieties of basil and all have a gingerish, clove-spice pungent scent. It is particularly delicious when served with tomatoes and gives a special flavour if added, in the last few minutes of cooking time, to tomato bredie. It improves many savoury dishes and, as it is only an annual, the leaves can be salted in layers in an earthenware crock, then rinsed and used as needed.

For salad dressings in winter, chop and macerate sprigs of basil and add to olive oil or maize oil or to white vinegar. Leave on a sunny windowsill for one month, shake and turn the jar every now and then, then strain and store.

Fresh basil pounded in a pestle with salt, garlic and olive oil, then added to pasta or other sauces, is the famous base for the favourite Italian pesto sauce.

If a pot of basil is placed on the kitchen windowsill and the herb is touched and bruised slightly each day, it will keep the room free of flies. I gather bunches of fresh basil on summer mornings and tie them in bundles and hang them in the kitchen. Even in mid-summer the flies stay away.

Basil is a strong tonic and antiseptic and is excellent for relieving nausea. The fresh leaves rubbed onto the temples help a headache and the Tswana use the dried leaves as a snuff to clear the head.

Long ago basil was used as a strewing herb and I have noticed that when drying basil on the racks, the ants and hornets flee the sheds and only return once the basil has been safely boxed and put away.

Sprigs of the wild basil which grows all over the farm are used to scent the buckets of rinsing water after washing is done on the river bank. The Tswana children put twigs of wild basil, with its heavy clove-like scent, into the buckets of water that they draw from the well and carry to their homes on their heads, as it keeps the water fresh and prevents slopping out of the bucket!

The smoke from burning basil is used as a mosquito repellent and often a few dried stalks, stripped and kept handy, added to the coals at an evening braaivleis, will keep all those troublesome mosquitoes and moths away.

Several African tribes use crushed and pounded basil leaves as a hair application, massaging it well into the scalp. Many believe that branches placed under their mattresses will aid sleep and keep the evil spirits away.

Six leaves of basil, crushed, to 1 cup boiling water is a good mouth rinse and gargle and will keep the mouth fresh, as well as cure thrush, mouth ulcers and bleeding gums. Rinse and gargle 10 times a day.

GRANADILLA

Passiflora edulis

Passion Fruit

The granadilla or passion fruit owes its name to its flower which resembles the instruments of Christ's crucifixion. The vine is useful for covering fences and the passion fruits ripen in summer and are delicious in fruit salad and summer drinks.

It is unable to stand heavy frost so should be well protected in winter. In Natal and along the coastal regions it grows prolifically and in protected positions in the Transvaal can live for many years.

The fruit contains a high vitamin C content and is used as a digestive stimulant. In Madeira the fruit is used as a remedy for gastric carcinoma.

The juice contains a huge amount of pectin and so jells quickly and this accounts for the rapid thickening of the concentrated juice. The rind too contains pectin and this will perhaps be of commercial use in the future.

For over a hundred years the leaves and flowers have been used medicinally, mainly as a soothing, nerve calming drink. The juice was considered a digestive aid in heartburn and indigestion and is now widely used in commercial drinks.

NETTLE

Urtica dioica

Stinging Nettle, Brand Nettle, Bobatsi (SOTHO), Umbabazane (XHOSA)

The nettle, so cursed and so widely spread throughout the world, is packed full of goodness. Records of the use of nettles can be traced back to the Bronze Age. The Greeks knew it as 'akalyphe' and the Romans as 'urtica' and they used it as a rheumatism remedy by flogging the painful area with nettle branches, thereby stimulating the blood flow to the afflicted part and thus aiding the removal of impurities by means of the increased blood flow. This method is still used today.

The leaves possess an acrid fluid, formic acid, which causes blisters and burning on the human skin but immediately the leaf is plunged into boiling water the hairs are rendered harmless and the leaf can be used in a number of ways.

Flagellation with fresh nettles is also used in gout, arthritis and paralysis and a tea made of the seeds and leaf has been used for internal haemorrhages, jaundice, urticaria, dysentery, bronchial catarrh, as a purgative and to treat haemorrhoids and oedema.

An infusion of the leaf is used in Europe even today as a blood purifier and expectorant, to help expel stones from the kidneys and to tone up the whole system, and as a remedy for anaemia, sciatica, arthritis and infertility.

Externally, a hair wash made from nettles is an excellent rinse and scalp massage which improves the colour and texture of the hair, and removes dandruff.

Even the dried powdered leaf is useful. It stops nosebleeds when used as a snuff, and the stems and leaves are used commercially in the manufacture of cloth and paper.

The young shoots and leaves can be made into a delicious spinach-like dish and added to soups and stews. This is one of the world's most chlorophyll-rich plants and should be eaten freely, as no other plant excels the nettle in vitamin and mineral content.

The dosages recommended for treating the above ailments are 4 handfuls of leaves and flowers (wear rubber gloves) to 1 litre of boiling water. Steep, strain and drink a wineglassful three times a day.

For hair rinse and scalp massage, use 2 cups of flowers and seeds, pressed down, to 4 cups of water, boiled and steeped and strained, then massaged well into the hair.

A cupful of flowers and seeds heated gently in 2 cupfuls of wine, strained and taken once a day, a wineglass at a time, serves as a blood cleanser and tonic and relieves internal haemorrhaging and excessive menstrual flow. A stronger brew can be made for the treatment of diarrhoea and worm infestation.

Black people use nettles as a green feed for cows and pigs, turning it into silage. They also cook and eat it themselves like spinach throughout the summer.

1 Mullein (*Verbascum thapsus*)
2 Elder (*Sambucus nigra*)
3 Ajuga (*Ajuga ophrydis*)
4 Fennel (*Foeniculum officinale*)
5 Wild strawberry (*Fragaria vesca*)

1

2

3

4

5

1

2

NETTLE SOUP

One large saucepanful nettle leaves and tops
45 g butter
60 g flour
1 litre good stock
salt and pepper

Cook the washed nettle tops in their own water for 10 minutes. Drain and chop. Melt the butter, add the flour and stir in the hot stock until it thickens. Simmer and season. Mix in cooked nettles and liquidize. Add a little more stock if it seems too thick. Serve with croutons.

1 Pomegranate *(Punica granatum)*
2 Maidenhair fern *(Adiantum capillus-veneris)*

ROSELLE

Hibiscus sabdariffa

African Mallow, Natal Sorrel, Dikelenge (ZULU), Umganganpunza (NDEBELE)

Roselle was used as a colouring and flavouring as early as 1774. The calyx of the flowers is the part used and in Switzerland, where it is known as 'Karkade', it is especially popular. It is used in wines and sauces, jellies and jams.

It is a bushy annual, reaching about two metres in height and does well in a tropical environment. It is native to tropical Asia but grows easily and readily in South Africa where it seems to flourish near Muden in Natal.

A soothing tea can be made from roselle and it is also an effective cough remedy, served with honey and lemon. The ruby-coloured tea is made from an infusion of the calyx. It contains citric acid.

The seed has been used as an aphrodisiac and the Zulu use an infusion to counteract the effects of alcohol. In East Africa the leaf is used as a wound dressing and as a diuretic. The Ndebeles use it for chest coughs.

Cold roselle tea sweetened with honey, 500 ml to 15 ml gelatine, makes a delicious jelly and is cooling and refreshing in summer. The stems yield an excellent fibre known as roselle hemp and it is grown as a crop for this purpose.

FEVERFEW

Chrysanthemum parthenium

Featherfew

Many, many years ago feverfew was used in the form of a tea as a general tonic. Its Latin name, 'februfugia', means a substance which drives out fever from the body. The whole plant is aromatic and has a pleasant scent. It is useful for pot-pourris as the daisy-like flowers dry well.

Feverfew is the famed 'women's herb' as it was used extensively in female infertility, female hysteria, to help in labour and retention of afterbirth and to promote menstruation, as well as as a suppository for painful piles. The dosage: make a standard brew of one large handful of dried herbs to two cups of water or two large handfuls of fresh herbs to two cups water. Place in an enamel pot with a lid, add the cold water, then heat over a gentle heat until boiling point is almost reached. Remove from stove and allow the herb to steep for at least three hours (overnight steeping is best). Then pour off the liquid. Keep the pot covered throughout the preparation and do not keep longer than two days. A wineglass should be taken three times daily.

Feverfew was once used as a mild sedative and an infusion is also a good cure for indigestion.

There has been much talk lately about the newly discovered uses of feverfew in regard to the treatment of migraine and arthritis, and the continued positive results are giving courage and help to many sufferers. The dosage is generally in the form of a tea made from 3 leaves to 1 cup of boiling water, taken three times daily.

A few chopped leaves added to the washing up water will lessen the grease or oils from dirty dishes.

Feverfew is an attractive garden plant and, being a biennial, sometimes perennial, it sets seed easily. It is rewarding to grow as a cut flower. With tansy flowers it is a marvellous fly repellent in the kitchen and they make a charming midsummer bouquet.

A GOOD SUMMER INSECT REPELLENT BOUQUET

Equal sprays of sweet basil, tansy flowers and feverfew in a large crock, placed on the kitchen dresser will keep the flies and mosquitoes out. Bruise the leaves from time to time.

PLANTAIN

Plantago lanceolata, Plantago major

Englishman's Foot, Fairy's Wand

All over the world plantain has been used for its wonderful healing properties. Pieces of root are used for earache, a decoction of the leaves for conjunctivitis, local application to wounds and sores, and a tisane made for general debility, constipation and diabetes.

Plantain is also a good stock feed and grows everywhere – along pavements in the busiest streets, at the edges of roads in the quiet country, at the verge of the sand dunes close to the sea and in every type of soil, sandy or clay.

There are over 200 varieties of plantain and now that research has proved there are antibiotic properties in the species, it is being looked at with new eyes.

Plantago major is made into a tea by both the Xhosas and the Zulus for diarrhoea and the fresh juice of the leaf is still believed to be an amazing cure for malaria, speedily bringing relief.

The young leaves can be eaten chopped into a salad, and a poultice made of pulped leaves and crushed root, warmed in a little water and applied on pieces of linen to boils and abscesses, is a sure healer. The Tswanas also use this same method for local application to piles.

I use plantain constantly as a rub, crushing a leaf or two, for bites and stings, nettle rash and mosquito bites. For bee stings and insect bites first remove the sting and, if outdoors, rub plantain leaves into the affected area. Plantain leaves can be bound in place, moistened with a plantain infusion (one handful of leaves boiled in 2 cups of water) or the pulped leaves of wormwood, sage, rosemary or rue. First warm and soften the leaves in warm water, then apply to the area, binding in place with cloths wrung out in warm water and vinegar (a mixture of equal parts).

The leaf has such amazing healing properties that it has long been used as a treatment for snake bite, dog bite and scorpion bite. At the other end of the scale, the seed is a good food for small birds.

The American Red Indians used to do a profitable trade peddling plantain ointment as a general cure-all.

SOAPWORT

Saponaria officinalis

Bouncing Bet, Fuller's Herb

Soapwort grows in every garden everywhere – a tiresome invader if you are unaware of its wonderful uses! Leaves, stems, flowers and roots contain saponins and, when boiled in water, the resulting soapy liquid can be used in many ways.

For hair that is split, dry, damaged and out of condition, wash in a strong concentrate, four handfuls of herb to 2 litres of rainwater. Rinse hair in rainwater in which either 2 sprays of rosemary (for dark hair) or a handful of chamomile flowers (for blonde hair) have been steeped. For hair that is dull and lifeless after an anaesthetic, make a brew of six handfuls of root, leaves and stems. Boil up in 2 litres of rainwater, stand until cool, remove the herb and in the same water, boil up another six handfuls of herb. Use this warm water after the usual shampoo and soak the hair in it for as long as possible, then rinse in clear, warm water.

Use soapwort for washing old fabrics and old tapestries, then rinse several times in clear, tepid water. It is also a valuable cleanser for wounds and grazes, skin rash and eczema. Boil up the freshly picked herb each time you use it.

Soapwort is poisonous to humans, animals and fish but there is a reference to the rootstock once having been used for rheumatics and as a febrifuge. If planted in an open-ended shallow drum or open pipe sunk into the ground, the roots will be contained and will not invade so readily.

WATERCRESS
Nasturtium officinale

Watercress grows in fresh running water or along the wet banks of furrows and it seems to do especially well where the soil has a high lime content. It is an introduced species to South Africa but has become half wild. Seed can be sown at any time during the spring and summer by just tossing the seeds along a river bank. One small packet of seed will mean watercress for ever, unless the wild duck and waterfowl find it!

The high vitamin C content of watercress makes it a desirable ingredient in summer salads and in the autumn watercress soup is delicious served with thick crusty slices of home-baked bread.

Watercress was used in the seventeenth century in a popular anti-scorbutic drink which contained orange juice and scurvy grass as well, and as it is such a tonic herb, it was used for rickets, anaemia, weak eyesight and to increase the milk flow in nursing mothers.

The Xhosas use watercress as an anthrax remedy for cattle. As soon as an anthrax pustule appears, a crushed leaf and stem is applied to the area and a vinegar-soaked cloth bandaged over it. For 24 hours this is kept in position and results in intense irritation. Then the bandage is removed and a new bandage soaked in vinegar is re-applied and this treatment is continued for 21 days. Thereafter a poultice of watercress is rubbed into the lesion and held in place by the vinegar-soaked cloth. By this time the lesion is healed.

The 1820 Settlers made a cough mixture by soaking crushed watercress leaves in honey and leaving overnight.

The Tswanas in the Transvaal use the leaves raw to assist menstruation in young girls. They also cook watercress and mix it with cabbage leaves for chest colds.

Watercress sandwiches on a hot summer afternoon are deliciously cooling and refreshing. The seeds germinate very quickly. Trays lined with wet cottonwool onto which watercress and mustard seeds have been sown should be placed on a windowsill and kept damp. They will soon sprout brilliant green leaves. Cut these off with a pair of scissors and use in sandwich fillings. This is always a special thrill for children as their little gardens come to life before their eyes and they enjoy cutting off the green tops for salads and garnishes. Successive trays can be kept going so that there is a good supply of sprouted seeds.

Watercress juice is an antiseptic cleanser and will help remove spots and blemishes. Pulp leaves and stems and apply the juice to the spot. Leave in position for 15 minutes then wash off with tepid water.

WATERCRESS SOUP

Gather a basketful of watercress from an unpolluted stream. Wash well in cold water to which a few crystals of permanganate of potash have been added. Place in a pot with a well fitting lid. Add a little water and bring to the boil. Add a chicken broth cube or a packet of chicken soup, adding more water if necessary. Next add a chopped onion, salt and pepper and some chopped parsley. Boil again for 10 minutes then put through a liquidizer and serve hot.

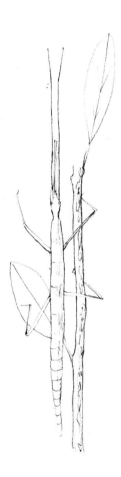

MINT

Mentha

The varieties of the Mentha species are so wide and numerous that they could fill a book. Perhaps the favourite mints are *Mentha aquatica*, *Mentha rotundifolia* (apple-mint) and *Mentha spicata* (garden mint).

Mentha aquatica is powdered and eaten by blacks with porridge for abdominal upsets, diarrhoea and dysentery. The Tswanas, the Xhosas and the Southern Sotho favour this variety for colds and coughs, drinking it in the form of a tea.

The Sotho place it under the bedding of an asthmatic or if someone has bronchitis or a chest cold, believing it to ease the breathing.

Mentha rotundifolia is much used in sauces and drinks, as is *Mentha spicata*.

All the mints are useful for headaches, nausea, upset stomach and for colds and 'flu. The standard brew is a handful of leaves to a cup of boiling water. Sweeten with honey. This can be taken several times a day.

Chopped mint leaves in salads are delicious and summer fruit drinks are greatly improved by the addition of mint leaves.

A mint tea taken at the end of a heavy meal will improve digestion, cure acid stomach, flatulence and all disorders of the digestive system.

Mint leaves rubbed over stiff, sore joints will bring ease and comfort and arthritis and rheumatism sufferers have found much relief in using mint as an external rub as well as a bedtime drink.

Steep mint leaves that have been crushed in apple cider vinegar for twenty-four hours and then use these leaves as a rub.

For a bad headache dip a cloth in this mint and apple cider vinegar lotion and lay it over the head. Renew it frequently. At the same time sip a little mint tea sweetened with honey and you will find that even the severest headache will be relieved.

Posies of mint hung in kitchen cupboards and in the pantry will keep them fresh and insect free.

Tumbleweed *(Boophane disticha)*

24

1

2

3

RUSSIAN TARRAGON

Artemisia dracunculoides

In early spring the first green spikes of tarragon push their way up through the soil and before long the feathery fronds are big enough to pick. The delicate flavour will enhance many a dish and tarragon vinegar is a firm favourite in many countries.

Tarragon is another herb of the Artemisia family and the Latin name 'dracunculus' is derived from the shape of the coiled dragon- or serpent-like root. It is native to Siberia and Asia and has been introduced into other countries. Its easiest propagation is by root division and it seems to thrive in almost any garden soil. Tarragon dies down in winter but can be dried and used in vinegars and salad dressings or sprinkled over chicken, fish and roasts throughout the winter.

Fresh tarragon stimulates the appetite and long ago it was used to soothe toothache.

It still has a place in the perfume industry and is commercially grown in America and in Europe. It is also used to flavour liqueurs.

TARRAGON VINEGAR

Choose a good, pure white vinegar. Into the bottles put 3 or 4 sprays of tarragon, picked in midsummer when the flavour is at its strongest. Seal and lay the bottles on their sides in the sun. A hundred hours of sunlight are needed to make a strongly flavoured vinegar. Every 20 hours of sunlight (count from 10 a.m. to 4 p.m. as the early morning and late afternoon sunlight is not strong enough) exchange the sprays in the bottle for fresh ones.

When ready, strain the vinegar through cheesecloth, bottle in attractive glass bottles, add a spray of fresh herb to the vinegar and seal well. Use in salad dressings and sauces.

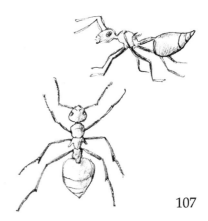

1 Bergamot *(Monarda didyma)*
2 Morning glory *(Ipomoea purpurea)*
3 Donkey's peach *(Araujia sericifera)*

107

BORAGE

Borage officinalis

Borage was believed to have originated in Syria but today it is widely cultivated all over the world and is often found growing wild.

The young leaves, chopped, are a healthy addition to salads and dipped in batter and fried are a favourite, easy-to-make supper dish.

Borage has always been associated with courage and cheerfulness. The knights of long ago always took borage with them wherever they went to give them courage and confidence. As the leaves are rich in potassium, calcium and mineral salts they make an excellent tonic, blood purifier and refrigerant.

The leaves are used for treatment of fevers, jaundice, coughs and bronchitis and a pulped poultice of the leaves is helpful in swellings and bruises. The leaves may also be used as a rub for wasp or bee stings, and the leaves were once believed to be so powerful that it was claimed that even scorpion bites, snake bites and the bites from rabid dogs could be healed by applying a borage poultice.

Today a brew of the leaves is still used as an excellent eye lotion for red, inflamed, sore eyes and also as a ringworm remedy. The lotion is made from a strong brew and is used as a wash. A bandage may be soaked in the brew and kept over the eyes at night for several nights running. During the day squeeze the juice from the leaves over the painful area.

Borage tea, made from half a litre boiling water poured over a handful of leaves and allowed to steep for a few minutes, then strained and sweetened with honey, is an instant reviver. This tea is excellent for chest colds, bronchitis and will cure a persistent cough. A cupful before bedtime ensures a peaceful night.

Borage has beautiful blue flowers with a perfect, exquisite design. They can be eaten in fruit salads or allowed to float in a bowl of fruit punch. They can also be crystallised and used as decorations.

The potassium that borage contains combats all inflammations and is particularly effective in stimulating the cortical area of the adrenal glands. It therefore helps the body make its own cortisone, so perhaps if one is treated with cortisone at any stage, borage should be seriously considered as a natural source!

Borage strengthens the nerves and is excellent in the treatment of kidney and bladder inflammation. Irritations, stresses and depressions may be soothed by eating borage, and it will induce peaceful sleep. It also clears the bloodstream and flushes and clears the kidneys.

Borage leaves make an appetising addition to soups and stews. Once you have a borage plant in the garden it will give you much pleasure and will seed itself readily. It seems to survive even the hardest winter; there are always some green leaves to gather for warming winter soups.

VINCA ROSEA

Lochnera rosea, Catharansus rosea

Pink periwinkle, Soldaatblom, Maandrosies

The leaf of this easily grown prolific plant is used as a diabetes remedy and was once used for rheumatism. Several pharmaceutical firms have over the years produced medicines using this plant and recently great fields of *Vinca rosea* have been grown in the Rustenburg, Transvaal, district, and the roots processed and dried and used in medicines for leukemia.

An infusion of leaves and flowers (3 leaves and 3 flowers per cup of boiling water) is the general way of using the plant but many people feel that it has no definite effect for the diabetic.

There are, however, positive results in cases of chronic constipation, using leaves and flowers in the form of a tea before retiring for the night.

Perhaps we should start to notice how easily vinca grows everywhere, even on the sand dunes at the sea, as this plant is proving to be one of our most valuable anti-cancer medicines. It is used when it is in full flower as that is when the active principles are at their most effective.

The Zulus use the milky sap for insect bites and for warts and they make a tea of the pink flowers for blood cleansing.

SUMMER AND AUTUMN

CASTOR OIL PLANT

Ricinus communis

The famed castor oil purge straight away makes one wary of this decorative plant. As children, we were so often warned of its poisonous seeds that I have always hesitated to have it in my herb garden.

On learning more and more of its virtues, however, I now plant it annually (the winter frosts kill it) and in sheltered places that are frost-free it reaches tree-like proportions.

The castor oil plant was called *Palma Christii* – Christ's hands – in medieval Latin as the healing powers in the leaf are so great that it was likened to Christ's healing hands.

Frequent applications of the leaf reduce warts and tumours and a warmed leaf applied externally to the tumour or wound, excluding all air and bound in place, has amazing drawing properties.

The oil is an excellent rub for bruises and will also prevent falling hair. It is most satisfactory in the treatment of ringworm, mange and skin ailments in dogs.

For the treatment of sore throats, swollen glands, mumps and stiff necks, soak a piece of cotton cloth in 1 cup of castor oil to which has been added 10 drops of lavender oil and 2 sprays of rosemary leaves. Spread the cloth out in a shallow pan and place in a warm oven. Wring out the cloth and apply as hot as can be tolerated to the throat. Keep it in place overnight with a lightly bound crêpe bandage.

In Zimbabwe the blacks use the skin of the bark for stitching up wounds, as well as a dressing for wounds and sores.

The juice from the stem is widely used as a toothache remedy. Pieces are chewed and then spat out, because if swallowed it is a powerful purge. Dr Jarvis, in *Folk Medicine*, uses castor oil as a rub on moles and blemishes. When rubbed on nightly it removes age spots, freckles and even moles and 'beauty spots'.

BIRDSEED

Lepidium africanum

Pepperweed, Sterkgras, Peppergrass, Sebitsa (SOUTHERN SOTHO)

This dainty little weed is one of my favourites. Ever since I was a child I carefully cultivated birdseed weed for our canary and tied little bundles together as a treat for him, held by a peg in his cage to allow him to pick off the seeds easily.

Birdseed is common throughout South Africa and the Zulus use an infusion of the root, stem and seeds as a cough remedy.

The Southern Sotho eat it as a vegetable when young, before it has set seed; stock find it equally tasty and it therefore has much value for grazing.

The seeds have a peppery taste and the whole plant, picked when the seeds are fully ripe and dried, makes a pretty lacy filler for dried flower arrangements.

ROSE-SCENTED GERANIUM

Pelargonium graveolens

The pelargoniums are varied and numerous and, in general, are regarded as beneficial in cases of dysentery and diarrhoea.

The leaves can be made into a tea and they can be used to flavour food and drinks. The favourite and most common for fragrance is the rose-scented geranium. I can remember stages where I became totally involved in the uses and fragrance, so much so that I gathered armfuls in the early summer mornings to rub onto the old farmhouse furniture and the wooden salad bowls and spoons. The imparted fragrance lasted weeks and weeks. I would bake sandwich cakes and baked custards and vanilla puddings, each flavoured with a rosette of geranium leaves placed at the bottom of the dish and cooked with all the rich taste and fragrance coming through the finished cake or pudding.

All through the summer I gather great bunches of geraniums and dry the leaves in the shade. All my pot-pourris, pillows and sachets have geranium leaves as one of the main ingredients. A special green pot-pourri is a favourite and I make clay pots encircled by a ring of cut-out clay geranium leaves with a large geranium leaf lid. The main ingredients are the rose-scented geranium and the peppermint geranium. This mixture is especially useful for clearing a smoky atmosphere.

At the end of a hot summer day it is pure joy to take the dogs for a walk in a field of geraniums. The air is heavy with the perfume and as the dogs run through the rows they become fragrant bundles of energy and always seem to sleep well after a run in the scented geraniums.

I experimented with pure geranium filled peace pillows and found that I too slept well on such a pillow. I replace the leaves from time to time and the fragrance is just enough to be restful and pleasant.

To make a more lasting fragrance, orris root and crushed cloves could be added to the geranium leaves, together with a few drops of geranium oil.

The blacks rub their carved wooden spoons and bowls with geranium leaves as the oil in the leaves makes a quickly absorbed polish, and leaves a fragrance that ensures a quick sale.

Geranium leaves rubbed into greasy, oily paint-stained hands will remove the dirt most effectively.

Wild pineapple (*Euchomis undulata*)

1

2

3

LOVE-LIES-BLEEDING

Amaranthus hypochondriacus

Pigweed, Misbredie, Hanekam, Thepe (TSWANA), Umbuye (ZULU), Umtyutu (XHOSA)

There are a number of Amaranth species native to tropical countries where they are used as pot herbs. In South Africa *Amaranthus caudatus* is used by blacks as a snuff plant and its seeds as a foodstuff, while its leaves are eaten as a spinach. The leaf is also used as a tea in the treatment of lung infections.

Amaranthus paniculatus is widely used in South Africa as a green vegetable. It is the favourite Tswana vegetable and they cook it with potatoes and onions for a healthy, nutritious addition to their daily diet.

In many countries it is cultivated as a grain and the seed is eaten by birds. Interestingly, a red ink is obtained from the seeds.

The *Amaranthus paniculatus* is also used as a tea in lung ailments and as a diuretic and is applied locally to scrofulous sores.

The attractive *Amaranthus hypochondriacus* – Love-lies-bleeding – which is often seen along the roadsides, derives its name from the Greek 'amaranton', which means 'not fading', as the crimson flowers do not fade when the plant dies. It thus became a symbol of immortality.

The dried flowering plant is still used today as a wash for ulcers and sores, as a gargle for ulcerated mouths and as a douche for leucorrhoea. It is also a valuable treatment for diarrhoea.

MOROGO SPINACH DISH

Gather a potful of young Amaranthus leaves and tips. Wash and cook in their own juices. Add 2 chopped or grated potatoes and a cupful of chopped green onions. Stir while cooking, adding a small amount of water. Add a little salt when serving.

1 Field mallow *(Malva parviflora)*
2 Lucerne *(Alfalfa)*
3 Periwinkle *(Vinca major)*

115

CLEAVERS

Galium aparine

Goosegrass, Lefero (SOTHO)

A climbing plant that seems to be found everywhere, cleavers has for centuries been widely used in folk medicine. It was mainly used in the treatment of all skin disorders and was beneficial in the treatment of wounds, ulcers, rashes and skin cancer. It is still used today as a lotion for cleansing acne and as a poultice for abscesses and cysts.

The Sotho use a brew of the stems and leaves for bilharzia and the Tswanas use it for the treatment of fevers and bladder ailments.

Cleavers is employed homoeopathically and a brew is beneficial in treating kidney and bladder ailments, and for generally clearing and toning the skin.

The fresh leaves and young tops make a wholesome vegetable and chopped young shoots can be delicious in soups and stews. The dried seeds can be roasted and ground and used as a coffee substitute.

Cleavers is rich in minerals and vitamins and will enrich the blood and promote urine flow. It is an excellent cure for insomnia and a brew used externally is comforting for sunburn and makes a good underarm deodorant as well.

Crushed fresh leaves and shoots are soothing to blisters and chafed skin, as well as minor burns and scalds.

A strong tea made of the whole herb is proving beneficial in the treatment of rheumatism and arthritis and for the removal of gravel and kidney stones. A cupful should be taken before meals. The leaves can also be eaten as a spinach.

The clinging habit of the leaves and stems makes cleavers a great favourite with the children. There is much enjoyment in decorating unsuspecting visitors with sprays of goosegrass!

TRAVELLER'S JOY

Clematis virginica

Old Man's Beard

A real pleasure in late summer is the traveller's joy, with its creamy wreaths of little flowers which twine along fences, into bushes and up into thorn trees. The green leaves and shoots are abundant all the year round, and even in winter they can be sought out in amongst the wisps and puffs of old man's beard, its fluffy seed form.

The leaves are vine-shaped and they were used as a tisane for weary travellers in the days of foot or horseback travel. Hikers and mountain climbers nowadays find traveller's joy a wonderful blessing. The tea made from the leaves will revive and refresh and a sprig of leaves and flowers infused in a water-bottle acts as a pick-me-up. As it cools, a linen cloth wrung out in the tea will help a headache, while the rest of the tea poured over travel-sore and weary feet relieves blisters or insect bites. Fresh leaves packed into the shoes will prevent blisters and aching feet and leaves placed in the crown of a hat will keep the wearer cool and fresh even in the heat of midsummer. Perhaps most important of all, leaves packed under a horse's saddle means no saddle sores.

FLEABANE

Erigeron canadensis

Canadian Fleabane, Cowstail, Bloodstaunch, Lehamu (SOUTHERN SOTHO)

Native to North America, fleabane is an introduced weed in South Africa with a tremendous nuisance value. It is estimated that one plant produces 120,000 seeds in a season.

Fleabane was widely used in orthodox medicine at one time and still today has a place in the treatment of several ailments.

The Southern Sotho use a decoction of the leaves and flowering tips in the treatment of sore throats and ringworm. They make a diluted lotion to bathe a sick child and use the same lotion for the washing of eczema areas.

Whites use a decoction of the plant in the treatment of diarrhoea and dysentery and as an application to wounds. A weaker solution is used to treat cystitis and genito-urinary diseases.

An infusion of the leaf has been found most effective in countering diarrhoea which develops in children who are allergic to milk.

Care should be taken, however, with sensitive skins. Fleabane is an irritant and the dry, powdered leaf is irritating to skin, eyes and mucous membranes. This irritant is due to the turpene that the plant contains.

Gallic acid and tannic acid are also present and these act as astringents. This is why the whole herb was used in the treatment of haemoptysis and haematuria, for it is tonic, styptic, diuretic and astringent.

Once, long ago, the seeds and dried leaves were thought to act as a flea repellent and were used with strewing herbs, the pleasant balm-like odour really being the only thing to commend it.

The Tswanas use the dried plant under their wood pile with khakiweed to deter ants.

SUNFLOWER

Helianthus annuus

The giant familiar sunflower, somehow so African, is native to Mexico and Peru and was later brought to Europe by Spanish explorers and still later introduced into South Africa as a quick food crop for livestock and poultry.

The vast fields of sunflowers, their brilliant yellow faces turned to face the sun, never fail to thrill and the flowerheads, easily measuring 30 cm across, are made up of hundreds of small florets packed tightly together, dripping with nectar.

Later, the shiny black seeds in their geometric rows, fitting so perfectly together, give enormous pleasure to the children (and the chickens!) who pick out each little seed, crack it and greedily munch the kernel. The kernel has a pleasantly nutty taste and, being 25% protein, rich in minerals and vitamins, makes a delicious addition to biscuits and tarts.

Oil extracted from the seeds is tasteless and odourless and is used as a salad and cooking oil and in the manufacture of margarine. It is said to be diuretic and expectorant.

The leaf has been used as a malaria remedy and a tincture of the leaf and flower petals has been used in bronchiectasis treatment.

In Italy the aerial parts of the plant are used as a diuretic, a febrifuge and a stimulant.

The lesser buds that grow off the main stem can be cooked and eaten like artichokes, with butter and vinegar.

Sunflowers draw large quantities of potash from the soil and when the dried stalks are burned the ash makes a good fertilizer.

In the autumn we cut off the great dried heads and put them out for the chickens and doves. The activity and greedy picking around the heads proves that they are indeed a treat.

The smaller heads, often the side shoots, picked when ripe and starting to dry, hung upside down to dry so that the heads remain erect, make interesting flower arrangements for the winter.

The yellow petals make a strong dye of bright yellow and an infusion of the flower can be used as a fly killer.

SOW THISTLE

Sonchus olearceus

Hare's Lettuce

Sow thistle may be a common weed throughout South Africa, but it is one with such healing properties that one is very pleased to see its appearance each year.

The whole plant is refrigerant and so is used in fevers and blood disorders. The juice may be applied to wounds and ulcers, as well as to acne and pimples.

Poultry and cage-birds love the thistle flowers and a small bunch gathered daily is consumed with relish by canaries.

The Tswanas on our farm gather the herb from the mealieland edges and feed it to their pigs. In times of vegetable scarcity they make a mild and pleasant spinach-like dish from the young leaves and flowering tops, flavoured with chopped onion.

I use it in salads as it is mild and pleasant and several people I have spoken to have talked of their grandparents using sow thistles for liver troubles and the treatment of jaundice and anaemia.

The juice is a white milk which makes a pleasant salve for sunburn.

A handful of leaves should be eaten daily for blood disorders and fevers.

120

MULLEIN

Verbascum thapsus

Our Lady's Taper, Blanket Herb

Mullein is an old-fashioned cottage garden plant and, once you have it, one which seeds itself readily and always looks decorative. The dried flowering spike can be dipped in fat and burned like a rush light.

The broad, grey, downy leaves are 'to line your slippers therewith' should you suffer from cold feet!

Mullein is valued for its curing properties of chest ailments – for coughs, pleurisy, pneumonia, bronchitis, tuberculosis, asthma and hayfever, as well as for all bowel complaints. Both the flowers and leaves are used in the brew and a small cupful of this tea, sweetened with honey, is drunk several times a day: 1 cup chopped flowers and leaves to 3 cups boiling water. Steep for 10 minutes, strain.

For inhalation purposes, sinus troubles, asthma or hayfever, place a heaped tablespoon of chopped fresh leaves in a kettle and boil. With a towel draped over the head, inhale the steam.

Mullein is also an excellent plant for making a home-brewed dye for natural fabrics.

121

BLADDER HIBISCUS

Hibiscus trionum

Lereletsane (SOTHO), Iyez-Lentshulube (XHOSA)

The flower of the bladder hibiscus is yellow, with a deep purple eye in the centre and it grows with ease along the edges of fields and in the veld all through the summer.

It is native to Europe and has become a common cosmopolitan weed of cultivation, but its bright yellow flowers attract bees and butterflies and gladden the eye, so perhaps we can forgive its nuisance value.

The leaf, warmed in hot water, is an excellent dressing for septic wounds and the Xhosas use it also for a roundworm remedy in animals and humans in the form of a strong tea made from the leaves.

The leaf is also used as an expectorant in bronchitis and chest ailments, again taken as a tea. To make this tea use four green leaves to 2 cups boiling water. Allow to stand, then drink a wineglass 3-4 times a day. Make a fresh batch daily.

The dried seed heads can be gathered and wired to use in winter bouquets.

122

1 Marjoram *(Origanum vulgare)*
2 Wandering jew *(Commelina beughalensis)*
3 Plantain *(Plantago lanceolata)*

1

2

3

1

2

3

FIELD BINDWEED

Convolvulus arvensis

This troublesome weed, native to Europe, is still used as a dressing for wounds, a tonic and cleanser of blood and was once used as a treatment for dropsy.

The dosages are two or three of the pink or white flowers eaten in a salad or a tablespoon taken morning and night of a brew made from the twisting stems and leaves.

In Italy and Vietnam the bindweed is used as a purgative and the whole plant is toxic to stock if eaten in any quantity.

The Tswanas pulp the leaves and apply these as a wound dressing; they too use the root as a powerful purgative.

The tonic tea is considered beneficial as a blood cleanser and here four flowers to a cup, sweetened with honey and taken once daily for two weeks is the correct dosage.

1 Mustard *(Brassica nigra)*
2 Chives *(Allium schoenoprasum)*
3 Buttercup *(Ranunculus multifidus)*

GRAPEVINE

Vitis vinifera

The grape, a symbol of health and fertility through the ages, is one of the oldest cultivated plants in the world. Its native habitat is the Caucasus, the Crimea and Asia where it grows wild. There are many cultivated varieties and all have wonderful, healthful properties.

Grape cures have proved little short of miraculous in cases of terminally ill people and the fruit, young leaves and tendrils contain so great an abundance of vitamins, minerals and healing substances that we should never be without a vine near at hand.

Vines clothe pergolas and walls, giving both shade and food and, in winter when the leaves drop, allow the welcome sunlight into the house. With the variety of types available beautiful and rewarding plantings can be made.

I grow long pergolas for a continual supply and the joy of the dense summer shade and the purple and green bunches of grapes hanging amongst the leaves is endless. Even the insignificant lime green flowers in the early summer give pleasure in the form of a rich heady perfume.

In the Transvaal a syrup effective in treating diptheria is made by boiling sugar and crushed grapes. The juice can be used not only in wine making but as a pleasant summer drink before fermentation.

The juice of the leaf is an effective eye-wash when diluted with water and the leaf and stem are astringent, containing a quantity of tartaric acid.

The oil extracted from the grape seed contains stearic, palmitic and melissic acids and has been recommended as suitable for making hypodermic solutions as it withstands sterilization by heat.

The juice of the grapes, fresh and undiluted, is used for the treatment of rickets, anaemia, dysentery, lymphatic ailments, impure blood, eczema, fevers, infertility, constipation and for dissolving internal growths, especially in the uterus.

Externally, grape juice can be used as a hair tonic, or for dressing a wound. In the latter case, the leaves are bound over the afflicted area.

As a general tonic a few tendrils should be chopped into the daily salad and as much fruit eaten fresh in the season as is desired. When grapes are out of season one should eat raisins and even drink wine!

A brew can be made of the leaves – 2 large leaves and a few tendrils to a cup of boiling water. Crush and steep, sweeten with honey and drink night and morning for the above ailments.

Vine leaves are delicious stuffed with chopped olives, brown rice and cream cheese. Place in an ovenproof dish, cover with a rich tomato and onion sauce and bake lightly.

SUMMER, AUTUMN AND WINTER

HORSERADISH

Cochlearia armoracia, Armoracia lapathifolia

The long, coarse leaves of the horseradish have a biting, pungent taste but the root is the medicinal part. Its hot properties make it valuable for expelling worms, destroying harmful bacteria and for stimulating the appetite. It also stimulates the circulation, and an increased blood supply means an increased rate of healing.

It has been used to dissolve internal tumours and the grated root may also be applied externally to swellings, tumours and wounds, bound in place with the fresh leaves. The leaves should be changed often for freshly grated root and new leaves.

For urinary and respiratory infections a daily dosage is one or two scraped and grated roots, divided into teaspoon amounts and taken on a piece of bread before meals.

The grated root is a delicious easy-to-make condiment. Dig out several roots, wash and scrape them and grate them finely. Pack into hot bottles. Pour a boiled brew of vinegar and strained spices over the grated roots and store for two months before using.

SPICED VINEGAR

1,5 litre vinegar
15 ml allspice
15 ml mustard seed
500 ml brown sugar
stick of cinnamon
15 ml cloves

Horseradish is strongly antibiotic, especially on the urinary tract and respiratory system, and it is anti-thyroid, like all the other mustard family herbs. This makes horseradish valuable in treating goitre, and excessive thyroid activity.

AUTUMN

COSMOS
Cosmos bipinnatus

Cosmos is a member of the *Asteraceae* family. It makes such a beautiful show of pink and white along our roadsides and in the fields that it simply could not be left out of this book.

To us cosmos means autumn and the end of summer. It means Easter, school holidays and travelling to the sea on pink and white lined roadways all the way down to Natal.

Cosmos is native to Central America and the West Indies and has become an introduced weed in South Africa.

Not only are the flowers in their varying shades of pink and mauve, deep red and white a soul-lifting sight, but they last well in water, too, and all along the farm roads we stop and gather great bunches and fill the house with fragrant pleasure all autumn long.

Some of the Tswanas tell us that they use the crushed, warmed leaves as a drawing poultice over abscesses, hard swellings and wounds and they say other African tribes do the same. They beat the leaves to a pulp and apply them, warmed, to the area, bound lightly in place.

Cosmos, then, has some medicinal value and, although the farmers curse it, it is truly a lovely sight that it is no wonder artists have been inspired to draw and paint it. Even children love to press the flowers and make drawings of them.

The white flowers in particular make an attractive Easter dinner table decoration with yellow and golden painted eggs tucked in around them.

GARLIC

Allium sativum

Ivimba-Impunzi (XHOSA)

Garlic is a member of the onion family and is universally used as a flavouring in cooking. The Egyptians and Romans used it medicinally and the slaves who constructed the pyramid of Cheops were fed garlic daily to sustain their strength.

There are several varieties of garlic, varying in flavour and strength, and its uses in medicine are as an antibacterial, an expectorant, for use in the treatment of hypertension, arteriosclerosis, dysentery, the common cold, typhoid and bronchial catarrh.

When the body is in normal health, garlic is useful as an antiseptic, general tonic and worm deterrent.

In fevers and blood disorders and the treatment of tuberculosis and whooping cough, asthma, obesity, rheumatism and arthritis, garlic has long been favoured and it has been a proven protection against many infectious diseases, including epidemic illnesses.

The Xhosas drink a decoction of the leaf and bulb as a febrifuge, sometimes adding *Artemisia affra*.

The plant mashed with honey and rubbed onto the afflicted area was a favourite remedy of the 'old people' for rheumatism.

A poultice of the bulb, applied to the temples, has been used as a headache relief and also for the relief of insect, scorpion and centipede bites.

In India garlic is rubbed over windowsills and around doorways to repel snakes and the warmed juice is used in drop form for earache. Diluted juice is used for the washing of wounds.

Inhalations of garlic have been a long-used treatment for all lung ailments, including tuberculosis, bronchitis and pneumonia.

Chopped garlic in the dog's food helps considerably to keep him free from ticks and fleas.

In most treatments it is preferable to eat garlic raw, chopping the leaves and cloves and adding to salads or eating on bread, but chopped garlic cloves can be added to bread dough before baking or to vegetables while cooking. Plenty of fresh parsley may be chewed to cleanse the garlic odour from the breath.

Dried garlic cloves maintain their medicinal properties for many months so it is easy to always have some at hand.

Finely chopped cloves are an essential standby for curing coccycidiosis in poultry.

ONION

Allium cepa

The onion has been in cultivation since AD 42 when Columella introduced the word 'unionem', from which the common word 'onion' is derived. Once it was probably native to central Asia or south-west India but its distribution is now worldwide.

It is an important plant as it contains vitamins A, B1, B2, B3, C and E. It has antibiotic properties, it is diuretic, antispasmodic, hypotensive and hypoglycaemic. The onion reduces blood pressure and the blood sugar level and is useful in the treatment of coughs, colds, bronchitis and gastric complaints.

Onion juice can be used externally to treat cuts and grazes, and also acne. Rubbing the scalp with chopped onion will promote hair growth. One of the old folk remedies was to bind onion slices around the throat to treat laryngitis or sore throats, with a strip of flannel to hold it in place.

In cookery the onion has no equal and its flavouring for soups, stews, meat and poultry dishes is so popular and necessary that it is easily available throughout the year, and can be bought anywhere.

Spring grown onions, pulled in the autumn and hung in bunches to dry, last until the following spring and, as they are easy and satisfying to grow, a row of onions in every garden is essential.

1 Sweet pepper *(Capsicum annuum)*
2 Horseradish *(Cochlearia armoracia)*
3 Pawpaw *(Carica papaya)*
4 Prickly pear *(Opuntia vulgaris)*

1

2

POMEGRANATE

Punica granatum

From the days of the early Egyptians pomegranates have been written about and illustrated. The fruit, the rind, the flowers and the bark from the stems have all been used medicinally by the Ancients and both Pliny and Dioscorides wrote of the root decoction as a tape-worm remedy, a remedy which blacks still use today for their children.

Punica in Latin means 'apple' derived from 'malum punicum', meaning 'apple of Carthage' and 'poma granata' means 'apple with many seeds'.

The pomegranate is native to Asia, Persia and the Himalayas and has become naturalized in South America, the Southern United States and parts of East and South Africa.

In South Africa a decoction of the dried rind of the fruit may be used for the relief of stomach-ache and in dysentery, and a weaker solution or infusion is taken for colitis. The infusion can be mixed with powdered rind and taken for diarrhoea and dysentery. As these preparations are all intensely bitter, they should be sweetened with a little honey.

The Mpondo use the root as a remedy for obstruction of the urinary passages, a decoction being made of the chopped root.

The bark of the branches is used in tanning leather as it contains a large amount of tannin. In Java the bark has been known to have been administered as a poison, as it is an irritant.

The flower and seeds of the pomegranate are also considered useful in the treatment of diarrhoea and some blacks use the leaf today as an external application to sores and skin grazes and inflamed areas.

Once, long ago the flower was used in dyeing, giving a violet-red colour. If a blossom is chewed it will give the same deep red colour to the saliva. It has, however, a bitter astringent taste.

The ripened fruit is used to make a refreshing summer drink called 'La Grenadine' but all our farm children prefer to sit in the shade and pick out the luscious, juicy, pink seeds and eat them that way, spitting out the solid kernels in showers once all the juice has been sucked out.

There are miniature forms of pomegranates which can be grown in pots and are very decorative, but the wild pomegranate is medicinally the most effective.

QUINCE
Pyrus cydonia

Found in 'old-fashioned gardens', the quince is often planted as a hedge. I have several quince trees edging my vegetable garden as I find them invaluable for jellies, jams and preserves.

The flowers in summer are an exquisite shell pink, and one of those country things that remind one of a happy childhood. Their sweet scent stirs the soul and I try to get the most out of their brief spring blooming.

The hard yellow fruit grows abundantly, bowing the shrub's slender branches as it ripens in autumn. The fruit is the medicinal part.

The brewed peel of the fruit makes an excellent hair tonic. Rubbed into the scalp it restores falling hair and generally tones up the scalp. Arabian horses' manes and tails to this day are washed daily in the brewed peel decoction for hair growth and as a tonic dressing. The same brew is used to wash all sores, insect bites and scratches – it is equally useful for human beings!

Grated, the raw fruit is excellent for diarrhoea and griping stomach.

QUINCE JELLY

2 kg ripe quinces
500 ml rainwater
10 allspice berries, crushed
juice of 6 lemons
sugar

Boil together the sliced quinces, allspice berries and water. Simmer for 40-50 minutes. Pour the quince pulp into a jelly bag or a piece of muslin in a strainer. Measure the juice and for every 500 ml of liquid, add 15 ml lemon juice and 500 g sugar. Boil briskly for about 10 minutes without stirring, skim off the surface foam, ladle into hot jars, seal and store.

QUINCE MEBOS (A tonic sweetmeat)

50 ripe quinces, sliced off the core, unpeeled
2 kg brown sugar

Combine ingredients with a small quantity of water to prevent burning. Cook until the quinces are tender. Mince the fruit and spread out on plates to dry in the sun. The autumn sun has enough heat in it to dry the pulp in a day. Roll up into tight rolls, wrap in adhesive plastic wrapping and store for the winter.

132

DONKEY'S PEACH

Araujia sericifera

Donkey's peach is a strong vine that twists through the trees and along fences. By autumn it produces heavy, oval green fruit, said to be loved by donkeys.

In winter the fruit bursts open, showering fairy-like seeds of gossamer all over the area. Small birds, such as preenias and sparrows, all gather the down for their nest linings and there is much activity in early winter as the fieldmice, too, gather the soft down for their hibernation quarters.

The plant has a thick white milk which oozes through the cut stem and the Tswanas use this for dabbing onto warts, with positive results. The dried open seed casings are useful in winter decorations.

CALABASH
Lagenaria siceraria

Calabash seed must be sown early in spring, direct into the ground, and covered with a heap of dried grass. This also helps to keep the surrounding soil damp.

Calabashes always need more space than one would think as the long trailing vines keep growing until the late summer.

The Tswanas and Zulus pick the young tips of the vines and make a nourishing vegetable from them. The leaves are washed and put into a pot with only the drops of water that cling to the leaves as the cooking water. A light sprinkling of salt is added and a dab of fat (usually mutton fat). Keeping the lid on, cook on a gentle heat, shaking the pot from time to time to turn the leaves in the fat. The dish is ready in ten minutes.

The young small calabash may also be eaten as a vegetable and it is very tasty. Steamed as a marrow, with salt and pepper and butter, it makes a delicious accompanying dish for tomato bredie or mutton stew.

The matured gourd in its many sizes and shapes is a valuable utensil and can even be used as a pipe which provides a cool, clean smoke and can be tailor-made for the smoker!

The most delicious sour milk or 'maas' is made in a big calabash. Using a mature, dried calabash, the stalk and a section below it are sawn off. Two notches are then cut into it to ensure a well fitting lid. The inside is scraped clean (the pips saved for next year's crop) and the calabash is filled with water, in which a cup of vinegar has been mixed, and left for a week. Then the water/vinegar solution is poured out and a wire pot-scraper is rubbed briskly all over the inside until it is quite clean. It is then left to dry thoroughly in the sun for two or three days.

Milk is then poured into the calabash and the lid notched into position. It should be left in a cool place, undisturbed for two days, or until the milk has thickened sufficiently. This creamy, thick milk should be spooned out and eaten with brown sugar and cinnamon, with stewed fruit for breakfast or, best of all, with strawberries and brown sugar.

When all the curd has been removed, the remaining whey is poured out and used for bread making. The calabash must then be washed out with hot water and left in the sun to dry until the next batch of thick milk is required.

African tribes all use calabashes in all sizes, as bowls, spoons and storage containers.

One of the most pleasurable country sights is a big earthenware pot of cool water standing under a thorn tree, a long-stemmed calabash 'spoon' beside it to scoop up a cool, refreshing drink in the midsummer heat. Nothing tastes quite so good or so natural.

134

BLINKBLAAR

Ziziphus mucronata

Mokgalo (TSWANA), Umphafa (XHOSA), Umhlahlankosi (ZULU)

Another herb tree, much used as a medicine, it is considered very important to have a blinkblaar tree growing near the home as it wards off lightning and keeps the evil spirits away!

The Zulus use the powdered leaf and bark in water as an emetic in chest troubles and a strong infusion is used for a cough.

Many tribes use the leaf as a poultice for boils, abscesses, carbuncles and other septic swellings.

In the Transvaal a decoction of the root is taken internally and a paste made from the leaves is applied to tubercular swellings.

For any sort of pain blacks frequently apply a poultice made from the baked and powdered root and then, after a period of time, usually overnight, they eat it.

A decoction made of the root and young shoots is given for measles and scarlet fever. Smoke from the burned root is also inhaled for relief of chest complaints. A brew made from the bark, and drunk frequently, is also effective.

A decoction of the leaf may be taken for lumbago and a poultice is then made from the leaves and externally applied to the affected area.

The edible berry is ground and made into a porridge-type brew, used as a coffee substitute, and in West Africa the berry is roasted and then ground into a coffee.

The bark is used by the Tswanas in tanning and the timber is used for ox yokes. The young flexible branches of the blinkblaar tree make good ox whips, the bark first being peeled from them.

The wood is also used for carving bowls and spoons and grain mortars and, as the wood is elastic, it has many uses, from fencing and gate making to sundry domestic uses.

Cattle and sheep browse happily on the leaves, despite the thorns, and monkeys, baboons and rock doves love the berries. Chewing a berry on a long hike is a sure thirst quencher.

On no account must the branches be cut after the first summer rains have fallen as it is believed that this will cause a drought.

PYRETHRUM
Chrysanthemum cinerarifolium

This plant is the source of one of the best known natural insecticides. The daisy-like flower is used as a spray dissolved in a suitable solvent for household use, in horticulture and for livestock. Crushed, dried leaves and flower heads can be sprinkled on stored fruit and vegetables and used quite safely around the house. Pyrethrum controls flies, mosquitoes, cockroaches, bedbugs and flying insects. It is rapidly toxic and paralysing to a wide range of insects but is non-toxic to mammals. One of its main uses has been in the form of a spray to kill the vectors of certain insect-transmitted diseases in aircrafts. Powdered flowers can be added to cement spray to cover walls in houses and warehouses in order to control pests.

The pyrethrins are concentrated in the flower head and the pyrethrin content increases with maturity.

Prolonged human contact with pyrethrum may lead to allergic dermatitis, rhinitis and asthma but I have used it for many years and have suffered no ill effects. Dried flowers behind rows of books, in the bookshelves or between papers and files are effective against fishmoths. Pyrethrum grows easily and is a lovely long-flowering garden flower. Fresh flowers last a long time in vases. Their crisp daisy heads never seem to droop, and after you have grown tired of the arrangement those same daisy heads can be pushed behind books and records to keep them insect-free.

Several commercial growers in South Africa and Kenya propagate by seed sown in the autumn *in situ* and thinned out the following spring. I find it transplants well and a row of pyrethrum grown between tomatoes and beans does much to combat insect infestation. Dried leaves of pyrethrum and khakibos sprinkled on and around tomato plants are amazingly powerful insect repellents and, as it leaves no poisonous residue on any plant or food to which it is applied, pyrethrum is particularly valuable to the organic gardener.

A small bag filled with dried flowers and leaves tied to a dog's basket or tucked into a kennel will combat ticks and fleas. Use a cheesecloth type of fabric and shake the bag daily to release the oils. Fresh dried flowers can be added from time to time.

Rub a handful of fresh flowers and a few sprays of rue into the dog's coat and you will be amazed at the exodus of ticks and fleas. Sprays of rue in the dog's basket are also effective. Replace these with fresh ones every few days if fleas are particularly bad and rub handfuls all over the basket and bedding.

THORN APPLE

Datura stramonium

Stinkblaar, Olieboom, Iloqi (ZULU), Lethsowi (SOTHO)

This unpleasant smelling annual is poisonous to stock and to humans, the fruit and seed being the most dangerous. It was used in folk medicine, however, as far back as 1750. It is indigenous to the shores of the Caspian Sea but has become naturalised in the Americas, Europe and throughout Africa. The Nubians once smoked the leaves for asthma and chest complaints and as the plant contains alkaloids comprised of atropine, hyocine and hyocyamine, whose action relieves spasms relating to bronchial asthma, it seems the ancient folk medicine really had something.

The Tswanas use the leaf, warmed, applied to local areas of pain, and the old people say that a spinach-like dish made from the very young plant results in 'symptoms of hilarity'!

Being toxic, however, there are many stories of poisoning and everyone is warned not to touch the plant. It grows readily anywhere and often the seeds contaminate mealiemeal and wheat, so farmers are careful not to allow a plant to mature in their fields.

Once, long ago, a whole school was poisoned in Lydenburg as the bread the children had eaten contained datura seeds. Military units, mine compounds, schools and orphanages have reported severe cases of datura poisoning, resulting often in death, the seeds having been in the mealiemeal or wheat used for baking. Children have been poisoned by sucking the nectar from the blossoms. Although it is a fascinating looking plant you would be well advised not to touch it.

LAVENDER

Lavandula spica

Lavender could be called a fragrant antiseptic necessity! For moth repellent lavender bags, making your drawers and cupboards fragrant, a wonderful cure for headaches, taken as a tea or inhaled, there is really no match for this joyful plant.

There are many varieties of lavender and all are medicinal. A tea of lavender leaves and flowers makes an excellent nerve tonic and is a pleasant nightcap after an anxious day. For the treating of headaches, sunstroke, vomiting or over-excitement, it has no equal.

Spread your washing over lavender bushes to dry in the sun and it will remain sweet-smelling and fresh for a long time. Use the stripped, dried stalks on winter fires and the whole house will be fragrant.

As far back as I can remember, my grandmother taught me to make tiny muslin bags and fill them with dried lavender flowers and leaves. Our linen always smelt of lavender and to this day I associate the pleasant summer smell of freshness, lavender and a contented childhood with my grandmother.

A flat lavender pillow beneath your bed pillow will do much to help sleeplessness, tension headache and restlessness. A steaming cup of lavender tea and honey last thing at night calms over-excitement and stress and you will awaken refreshed, and full of *joie de vivre*!

In autumn the butterflies are constantly busy over rows of lavender bushes and only the covering of winter grass to protect them from the frosts deters them.

Lavender is a delightful plant and an essential one in every herb garden. Propagate by cuttings in the autumn or sow from seed in shallow trays and harvest in autumn.

A CHEERING LAVENDER TEA
(For indigestion, sleeplessness, depression and anxiety)

One handful each:

lavender heads
garden mint or peppermint
melissa

Mix, dry and crush finely. Store in an airtight bottle. Use as ordinary tea, a heaped teaspoon to a cup. Sweeten with honey.

Mentha species
1 Spearmint *(Mentha aquatica)*
2 Catnip *(Nepeta cataria)*
3 Garden mint *(Mentha spicata)*
4 Pennyroyal *(Mentha pulgium)*
5 Peppermint *(Mentha piperita)*

31

1

2

SPIRITS OF LAVENDER (A tonic lotion)

60 ml dried lavender flowers
2 grated nutmegs
20 ml cinnamon, powdered
30 ml sweet cicely leaves, dried

Crush all ingredients together finely in a mortar. Add a quart of pure alcohol or, if unobtainable, cane spirit. Pour into dark glass bottles and seal tightly. Allow the mixture to stand in the sunlight for two weeks, shaking vigorously once or twice daily. This lotion applied on cloths that have been wrung out in cold water is excellent for allaying head-aches and soothing fevers when placed over the forehead.

OLD-FASHIONED LAVENDER BAGS

500 g lavender flowers
500 g lavender leaves
100 g powdered orris root
10 drops of lavender oil

Mix all ingredients together and seal in a plastic bag for a month, shaking daily. Then sew into small bags and spread them about in your linen cupboard.

1 Sour fig *(Carpobrotus edulis)*
2 Purslane *(Portulaca oleracea)*

WINTER

ELDER

Sambucus nigra

The elder is a magic tree. All parts are medicinal. An ancient belief was that the elder kept witches away and most houses would have an elder tree growing near it. Apart from chamomile, there is no plant that has been revered more than the elder for its medicinal properties.

The root, soaked in water, is used for kidney ailments. It can also be crushed or flaked and made into a tea which is good for swollen glands.

The bark, dried and powdered, is used in wine for epileptic fits, a wineglassful being taken in quiet periods.

The leaves make a tea, a green brew which can be wiped over arms and legs to keep mosquitoes and insects away. It is also good for baby rash and eczema. The brew is made of 750 ml leaves to 1 litre water, boiled, cooled and strained.

The same brew, strengthened with the addition of equal quantities of scented geranium leaves and 2 – 4 cloves of garlic, makes a potent skin remedy to cure bites and itches, rashes and ringworm.

The flowers make elderflower face cream, a hair rinse, and will soothe burns, scalds and sores. Elderflowers made into a brew are soothing for colds, bronchitis, influenza and pneumonia.

ELDERBERRY MULLED WINE

1 bottle red wine, port or claret
2 heads elderberries
1 stick cinnamon
125 ml brown sugar
7 cloves
2 heads elderflowers

Pick off berries and flowers. Mix all ingredients and simmer gently for 20 – 30 minutes. Strain through fine cheesecloth. Bottle and keep for one month. Serve warmed, in front of a fire at the end of a hard day's work.

Elderberries pounded up with honey make a healing and soothing salve for sore throats and coughs. Berries can also be applied, crushed, to burns and scalds.

ELDERFLOWER FRITTERS

Whisk together:
125 g flour
pinch of salt
1 egg white, beaten
125 ml warm water
5 ml baking powder

Dip heads of elderflowers into the batter and fry in oil until golden brown. Drain on kitchen paper and dredge with icing sugar. Serve with whipped cream.

ELDERFLOWER CHAMPAGNE

5 litres water
750 g sugar
3 lemons, peeled and sliced, plus juice of 3 lemons
6-10 large elderflowers

Boil together water and sugar with lemon slices and rind. Place flowers in lemon mixture and remove from stove. Let it stand for 24 hours, strain through cheesecloth, bottle and cork well. It will be ready to drink in a fortnight. Serve cold.

ELDERFLOWER TEA *(For heavy colds and influenza)*

30 g elderflowers
15 g peppermint leaves

Pour 1 cup boiling water over the flowers and leaves and infuse for a few minutes. Strain into a cup and sweeten with honey.

ELDERFLOWER FACE LOTION

Pour 250 ml boiling water onto 1 heaped tablespoon of dried elderflowers, cover and leave to cool. Strain into a screwtop jar and keep in the refrigerator. Use night and morning dabbed onto the face with cottonwool and allow to dry on the skin.

This lotion is good for tightening the skin and is soothing for sunburn and heat flush.

Ten large flower heads, fresh, boiled in 6 litres of water, is an excellent lotion in which to wash the face, using a pure soap. It cleans a greasy skin and is good for acne.

ORANGES AND LEMONS

Living near a citrus growing area, Rustenburg in the Transvaal, one cannot help but become involved in the many delights the citrus family has to offer.

Orange blossom in the spring has a heady perfume and we gather basketsful of fallen blossoms after the spring wind and the first rains.

Oil of neroli is obtained from orange blossom and the oil obtained from the young unripe fruit and the leaf is known as petitgrain oil.

In aromatherapy this fragrance is considered calming and sedative and eau-de-cologne owes its spicy note to its neroli and petitgrain content.

Dried, crushed orange, lemon, naartjie and grapefruit peel is a fixative used in pot-pourris. We dry the peels in the sun on wire racks and then put them through a hammermill. The dried, crushed leaves are also useful in pot-pourris and pomanders.

The traditional pomander, which remains effective even after several years, is a clove-studded Valencia or Seville orange which has been rolled in powdered orange peel and orris root. Hung in cupboards the fragrance is quite lovely.

It is also a moth repellent and clears musty air. Pomanders hung from pantry shelves will keep the room fresh and pleasant.

Making pomanders in front of a blazing fire on a chill winter's evening, pressing the cloves into the warmed and softened orange, remains one of those precious country crafts that soothe the soul.

ORANGE POMANDER

Warm and soften a Seville orange by pouring boiling water over it. Leave a few moments in the hot water, then take it out, dry it and roll it around in your hands. Then, using a steel knitting needle, prick holes in the skin, close together, and press cloves into the holes, leaving a central 'cross' free for the ribbon. About 25 whole cloves are needed for each fruit. Once the cloves are pressed in, roll the orange in a mixture of dried, powdered orange peel, orris root (equal quantities), and ¼ part powdered cinnamon. The easiest way to do this is to put all ingredients, orris root, powdered peel and spices, into a brown paper bag and shake it all together well. Leave the bag closed and put it on a warm windowsill to dry. Shake it up each day for a week and then keep the paper bag, still with its fragrant contents, in a dark airy cupboard until it is quite dry and hard.

Finally, take out the orange and tie a velvet ribbon around it in the central open part you left free of cloves and hang the pomander in your wardrobe.

Lemon pomanders and tiny kumquat pomanders can be made the same way. The little kumquat ones are quick and easy to make and a thin string can be threaded

144

through them with a large darning needle as there is not really enough space to tie a ribbon around the fruit. A cluster of kumquat pomanders are most charming hanging from the kitchen shelves or over the kitchen fireplace in the winter; the lovely fragrance brought out by the warmth of the fire will fill the room.

Pomanders were first recorded in France before the sixteenth century and, as scents, had a direct bearing on health. Pomanders and cassolettes were carried to ward off diseases. The French name 'pomme d'ambre', meaning apple of amber, was the name given to small balls of ambergris and scented herbs and spices that courtiers and those of high office carried about and sniffed to ward off disease.

The citrus pomander was carried by priests, physicians and judges who came into contact with the people and the ever present risk of plague.

POMANDER BEADS

Beads made with rose petals, lemon peel and cloves and worn next to the skin give off a lovely soft fragrance and with age can be polished into a very unusual necklace.

50 scented roses, wilted but still soft and pliable
sufficient rosewater to moisten
2 cups crushed lemon peel
¼ cup ground cloves

In a pestle and mortar, pound and mix the roses, lemon peel and ground cloves. Moisten with rosewater and several drops of rose oil until sticky. Using hands which have been moistened with rosewater, mould the mixture into beads. Pierce with a needle and thread while still soft. Leave on wax paper to dry in a cool place.

The medicinal uses for lemons cannot be overlooked. For whitlows or infection of the nails heat a whole lemon gently in hot water. Remove the lemon and make a tunnel down the centre. Pack the tunnel with common salt and fresh pine-needles. Bury the affected finger in the tunnel and keep it there for as long as possible. This treatment can be repeated whenever necessary.

For the treatment of colds, 'flu and coughs slice two lemons in half and place cutside down in a shallow dish of honey. Add two sprigs of rosemary and a few cloves and press these down into the honey. Leave overnight, then squeeze out the lemon juice and pour the honey, rosemary and cloves, mixed with the lemon juice, into a screw-top bottle. Take 1 teaspoon every half hour until the cough and feverishness has been alleviated.

In the kitchen citrus preserves remain firm favourites:

ORANGE MARMALADE PRESERVE

Choose perfect oranges. Peel thinly or grate off a little of the rind. Rub with salt. Allow to stand for two hours. Pour boiling water over the oranges and allow to cool down. Remove the centre of each orange with an apple corer. Squeeze out the pips. Place the fruit in fresh water and stand overnight. Place in boiling water and boil until the rind is tender and can be easily pierced with a matchstick. Remove and drain. Boil up a syrup made of 500 g sugar to every 500 g fruit and 3 cups water to every 500 g sugar. Boil the fruit in the syrup until it appears transparent and the syrup thickens. To prevent crystallization on the shelf add one cup of lemon juice to every 1,5 kg fruit and boil with the fruit. Bottle and seal in hot, sterilized jars.

KUMQUAT MARMALADE

Gather a basketful of kumquats. Slice thinly. To every heaped cup of fruit add three cups of water. Cover and stand for 24 hours. Then boil for one and a half hours. Stand overnight. Weigh the fruit. For every 500 g fruit add 500 g sugar. Stir well. Cook for about two and a half hours on a medium heat. Stir with a wooden spoon. Bottle while hot. Cover with brandied paper and seal well.

LEMON MARMALADE

Take 20 lemons or limes and the weight of the fruit in sugar. Slice the lemons thinly. Add 3 cups of water to every 2 cups of sliced lemons. Stir until the sugar dissolves. Stand overnight. Boil rapidly the next morning until the rind is soft and the syrup is jelly-like when tested. Bottle while hot and seal.

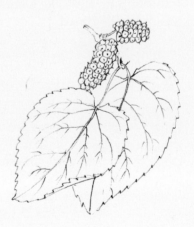

FENNEL

Foeniculum officinale

Fennel is primarily used to relieve all gastric ailments, including constipation. It is also helpful in fevers, cramps, rheumatism, obesity and diabetes.

A lotion made of 45 g chopped leaves to 1 litre water, boiled and cooled, is excellent for bathing tired eyes. Three wineglasses of this same brew taken daily is a good general tonic. It is also believed to aid memory and digestion.

The root is an excellent laxative, as is the heart of the shoot. The root must be grated finely and taken before meals, mixed with a tablespoon of bran for improved effect.

The seed is an antiseptic and 2 teaspoons of finely crushed seeds to a cup of boiling water will help speedily expel poisons from the body after a snake, dog or insect bite. Chopped leaves can be applied externally as a poultice to a suppurating wound.

As a slimming aid fennel tea is excellent. This is made using 1 dessertspoon chopped leaves per cup of boiling water and should be taken three times daily. Chopped fennel hearts and leaves in the daily salad are also beneficial.

The heart is a delicious vegetable when steamed and served with a white or cheese sauce.

CABBAGE

Brassica oleracea

Cabbage is well known as a winter vegetable but it has its medicinal uses too.

A warmed cabbage leaf without its midrib is a marvellous wound poultice or bed-sore dressing, and will soothe a burn.

The juice of the crushed inner leaves may be used to treat dogs with mange.

The green outer leaves of the cabbage are nutritious as they contain vitamins A and B. As the cabbage contains sulphur its seeds contain antibiotic substances, and the volatile oil which is formed when the seed is macerated in water, and which is related to mustard oil, contains antibacterial and antifungal principles.

As a drawing poultice a warmed cabbage leaf placed over the area is soothing and helps to draw the infection out. The leaf should be replaced hourly with a fresh one. If applied to bedsores the poultice can be kept on overnight.

HERB AND AILMENT CHART

There is a wonderful science in nature, in trees, herbs, roots, seeds and flowers which man has not yet fathomed. In nature God has provided a remedy for every disease that might affect us.

Jethro Kloss

ABSCESS:	plantain, violet leaves, field mallow, nasturtium, chickweed, cosmos, thyme.
ACHES AND PAINS:	nettle, comfrey.
ALLERGY:	rooibos.
ANAEMIA:	amaranthus, sow thistle, parsley, carrot, watercress, grape, nettle, purslane.
ANTIBIOTIC:	hypericum, plantain, nasturtium, onion, garlic.
ANTISEPTIC:	shepherd's purse, watercress, mustard, sour fig, basil, thyme.
ARTHRITIS:	nettle, parsley, wild strawberry, honeysuckle, feverfew, garlic.
ASTHMA:	mullein, mistletoe, speedwell, thorn apple, honeysuckle, garlic, mint, pawpaw.
ASTRINGENT:	periwinkle, peppermint, common groundsel.
BEDWETTING:	marjoram, catnip.
BILHARZIA:	cleavers.
BLADDER AILMENTS:	wild strawberry, mealie, southernwood, kweek, wandering jew, nasturtium, cleavers, carrot, asparagus, buchu, parsley, fleabane, Job's tears, wild olive, borage, pawpaw.
BLEEDING:	shepherd's purse, yarrow.
BLOOD CLEANSER:	aloe, nettle, borage, cleavers, sow thistle, field bindweed, morning glory, grape, mustard, wild strawberry, kweek, purslane.
BLOOD POISONING:	wilde als.
BLOOD PRESSURE:	shepherd's purse, onion, purslane, rosemary.
BOILS:	tumbleweed, prickly pear, arum lily, violet leaves, nasturtium, onion, chickweed, mealie, thyme, castor oil leaves, pawpaw.
BRONCHITIS:	wilde als, thyme, borage, elder, comfrey, garlic, bladder hibiscus, nettle, mistletoe, pennyroyal, yarrow, mullein, sunflower, Job's tears.
BRUISES:	field mallow, hypericum, marjoram, buchu, borage, wandering jew, comfrey, castor oil leaf.

150

BURNS:	aloe, agave, tumbleweed, arum lily, bulrush, violet leaves, sour fig, ivy.
CALLOUSES:	ivy, sow thistle.
CALMING:	rock rose, rose, scented geranium, melissa.
CANCER:	rock rose, parsley (preventative), carrots, violet leaves.
CHEST AILMENTS:	maidenhair fern, chickweed, bladder hibiscus, blink-blaar, peppermint, mullein, pretoriabossie.
CHILLS:	yarrow, thyme, mullein.
COLDS:	citrus fruit, elder, mustard, peppermint, wilde als, roselle, sage, yarrow, pennyroyal, mint.
COLIC:	quince, pomegranate, wild olive, peppermint, thyme, rooibos, blackjack.
CONSTIPATION:	dock, plantain, pawpaw, grape, castor oil, peppermint.
CONVULSIONS:	rue.
CORNS:	wild olive, ivy.
COUGH:	blinkblaar, marjoram, onion, mint, peppermint, lemon, borage, roselle, pawpaw, oranges, mullein, thyme, wilde als, watercress, maidenhair fern, comfrey, buttercup.
	whooping cough: thyme, prickly pear.
	expectorant: violet leaves, nettle, pepperweed.
CRAMP:	yarrow, mint.
CUTS:	hypericum, yarrow, common groundsel.
CYSTITIS:	southernwood, fleabane, parsley, kweek.
DEODORANT:	cleavers, parsley.
DIABETES:	parsley, plantain, prickly pear, vinca rosea, purslane, mulberry, fennel.
DIARRHOEA:	mint, fleabane, carrot, hypericum, plantain, comfrey, yarrow, quince, pomegranate, nettle, vinca rosea, sour fig, thyme, amaranthus, blackjack, pretoriabossie.
DIURETIC:	bulrush, amaranthus, fennel, celery, asparagus, onion, yarrow, mealie, roselle, sunflower, kweek.
DIZZINESS:	rue, lemon verbena.
DYSENTERY:	fleabane, grape, shepherd's purse, speedwell, hypericum, Job's tears, pomegranate, pawpaw, nettle, wild strawberry, sour fig, yarrow, bulrush, garlic, fennel.
EARACHE:	wilde als, shepherd's purse, hypericum, pig's ear cotyledon, yarrow, rue, ivy.

ECZEMA:	soapwort, wild strawberry, elder, wheatbran, comfrey, tumbleweed, grape, rosemary.
EYE AILMENTS:	wilde als, watercress, speedwell, cornflower, grape leaves, rue, celery, fennel, carrot, wild olive, field mallow, ivy, wild strawberry, chickweed, borage.
FAINTING:	hypericum, peppermint.
FEVER:	wilde als, feverfew, yarrow, grape, sage, lavender, ivy, thyme, purslane, borage, sow thistle, buttercup, marjoram.
FLATULENCE:	parsley, quince, asparagus, peppermint, sage, lemon verbena, pennyroyal, mint, celery, catnip, fennel.
FRACTURES:	comfrey.
GARGLE:	rock rose, dock, peppermint, sage, sour fig, amaranthus, marjoram.
GOUT:	wilde als, nettle, wild strawberry.
GRAZES:	speedwell, cornflower, yarrow, pomegranate, common groundsel.
HAEMORRAGE:	hypericum, periwinkle.
HAEMORRHOIDS:	wilde als, chickweed, pawpaw.
HAIR TONIC:	quince, grape, nettle, sage, basil, rosemary, castor oil.
HAYFEVER:	mullein, peppermint, pennyroyal.
HEADACHE:	violets, lavender, wilde als, wild olive, purslane, peppermint, marjoram, rosemary, thyme, basil, rose, garlic, pennyroyal, mint, ivy. *migraine:* feverfew.
INDIGESTION:	feverfew, granadilla, lemon verbena, chickweed, cornflower, sage, sweetpepper, kweek, pawpaw, mint, thyme, catnip, fennel.
INFLAMMATION:	pig's ear cotyledon, prickly pear, ajuga, garlic, blackjack, pretoriabossie.
INFLUENZA:	wilde als, nettle, pennyroyal, mint, thyme.
INSECT BITES:	borage, wheatbran, chickweed, fennel, dock, arum lily, parsley, cornflower, plantain, elder, quince.
INSECT REPELLENT:	cayenne pepper, southernwood, wilde als, khakibos, feverfew, pyrethrum, rue, garlic, agave, elder, sage, lavender, basil, rosemary, pennyroyal, fleabane, wild olive, peppermint.
INSOMNIA:	cleavers, rosemary, thyme, lavender, marjoram.

152

ITCHING:	elder, pennyroyal, soapwort, thyme.
JAUNDICE:	parsley, borage, speedwell, hypericum, asparagus, celery, carrot, rue, nettle, wild strawberry, ivy, sow thistle, fennel, marjoram.
KIDNEY AILMENTS:	southernwood, asparagus, borage, parsley, shepherd's purse, carrot, elder, Job's tears, mealie, pawpaw, fleabane, nettle (to expel kidney stones), lucerne, wild strawberry, nasturtium, celery.
LUNG INFECTIONS:	amaranthus, comfrey.
MEASLES:	blinkblaar.
MENSTRUATION:	southernwood, carrot, feverfew, yarrow, peppermint, rue, pennyroyal, thyme, wandering jew, catnip. *if profuse:* field mallow, nettle. *to induce:* asparagus fruit.
MUMPS:	ivy.
NAUSEA:	lemon verbena, pennyroyal, mint, basil.
NERVES:	thyme, field mallow, periwinkle, peppermint, melissa, cornflower, granadilla, violet, nasturtium, wild strawberry, celery.
NEURALGIA:	comfrey, thyme, celery.
NOSE PROBLEMS:	*bleeding:* shepherd's purse, nettle, periwinkle, thyme. *blocked:* peppermint, sage.
OBESITY:	fennel, sage, celery, garlic.
PAIN:	thorn apple, tumbleweed, blinkblaar, garlic. *abdominal:* wild pineapple (euchomis), catnip.
PNEUMONIA:	comfrey, maidenhair fern.
POST OPERATIVE:	hypericum.
PURGATIVE:	field bindweed, nettle, violet leaves, wilde als, agave, aloe, pretoriabossie, morning glory.
RASH:	speedwell, elder, tumbleweed, ajuga.
RELAXANT:	cleavers, peppermint, melissa, sage, mint, ivy, lavender, marjoram.
RHEUMATISM:	honeysuckle, garlic, agave, wild olive, sweet pepper, buchu, ajuga, pawpaw, rue, chickweed, mint, Job's tears, blackjack, comfrey, thyme, asparagus, parsley, celery, marjoram, pretoriabossie, hypericum.
SCIATICA:	hypericum, ivy, cabbage leaves, celery.
SEDATIVE:	orange oil, feverfew, sweet pepper, rosemary, wandering

	jew, scented geranium, lavender, lemon verbena.
SINUS:	pennyroyal, mullein, sage, peppermint.
SKIN DISORDERS:	honeysuckle, aloe, chickweed, wheatbran, thyme, buttercup, cleavers, dock, watercress, sow thistle, elder, comfrey, yarrow, pawpaw.
SLIMMING:	parsley, sage, fennel, garlic.
SORE THROAT:	rock rose, wild olive, nasturtium, honeysuckle, sage, onion, sour fig, buttercup.
SORES:	onion, amaranthus, periwinkle, arum lily, nasturtium, honeysuckle, carrot, chickweed, mealie, plantain, quince, tumbleweed.
STIMULANT:	sweet pepper, sunflower, peppergrass, buchu, borage, basil, wild asparagus, grape, nettle, garlic.
STINGS:	plantain.
STRESS:	rue, violet, periwinkle, lemon thyme, lemon verbena, rose, garlic, lavender, rosemary, melissa, sage.
STYES:	field mallow.
SUNBURN:	cleavers, sow thistle, comfrey.
SWELLING:	borage, carrot, field mallow, horseradish, ivy, cosmos. *swollen glands:* elder.
TONIC:	field bindweed, dock, sage, shepherd's purse. *heart:* rosemary.
TOOTHACHE:	wilde als, pig's ear cotyledon, yarrow, rue, tarragon.
TUMOUR:	grape, ivy, castor oil, nasturtium, celery.
ULCERS:	amaranthus, honeysuckle, chickweed, comfrey, carrot, lucerne, sow thistle, speedwell, aloe, yarrow, sage.
VAGINAL DOUCHE:	field mallow, amaranthus.
VARICOSE VEINS:	carrot, elder.
VOMITING:	buttercup, rooibos.
WARTS:	donkey's peach, castor oil, pawpaw, mistletoe.
WORMS:	horseradish, field mallow, thyme, pomegranate, hypericum, nettle, elder, garlic, bladder hibiscus, *ringworm:* dock, borage.
WOUNDS:	cosmos, field bindweed, mealie, grape, field mallow, periwinkle, honeysuckle, onion, chickweed, horseradish, mulberry, fleabane, soapwort, comfrey, carrot, hypericum, plantain, rosemary, yarrow, sow thistle, arum lily, bulrush, kweek, blackjack, castor oil, cabbage.

INDEX

BIBLIOGRAPHY

Bairacli-Levy, J de. *The Illustrated Herbal Handbook*. London: Faber and Faber, 1974.

Stuart, M, ed. *The Encyclopedia of Herbs and Herbalism*. New York: Grosset and Dunlap, 1979.

Watt, J M and Breyer-Brandwyks, M G. *Medicinal and Poisonous Plants of Southern and Eastern Africa*. 2nd edition. Livingston, 1962.